YES, HEALTH MINISTER

YES, HEALTH MINISTER

40 Years Inside the NHS Working for Children

Dr Sonya Leff

Book Guild Publishing
Sussex, England

First published in Great Britain in 2006 by
The Book Guild Ltd
25 High Street
Lewes, East Sussex
BN7 2LU

Typesetting in Bembo by
Keyboard Services, Luton, Bedfordshire

Printed in Great Britain by
CPI Bath

A catalogue record for this book is available from
The British Library

ISBN 1 84624 015 8

Contents

Chapter One

Why Write?

1948 'These are doctor's hands,' intones my grandmother, caressing my eight-year-old hands in her warmly loving, hard-working ones. 'These are doctor's hands. They'll never wash the dishes!' In my grandmother's generation the height of gentility was to employ a visiting maid, in cap and apron, to wash the dishes. The family had achieved this for a spell when my mother, an only child, was growing up. However, by the time we three grandchildren were on the scene after the Second World War, the maids had vanished. I had the happy privilege of belonging to the youngest generation of a three-generation household. My maternal grandparents were there when I was born; both were still there when I left home in my twenties for my student digs. Granny, with much love and pleasure, had prepared, cooked and served food to the seven of us in our family every day and that was in the days before freezers and microwaves. Together, she and I washed the dishes.

1998 Women's lives have certainly changed dramatically, with outcomes that could never have been foreseen. I was musing on this at a Department of Health seminar aimed at boosting women doctors 'through the glass ceiling'. With Granny's soft caress still, half a century later, imprinted in my mind, I found myself thinking, 'These are doctor's hands ... yes, they wash the dishes.'

After my retirement, to my surprise, I found that I was sleeping for fourteen hours in every twenty-four. Without the alarm clock, I never woke before 10 a.m. and even then my husband encouraged me to lie down for a bit after lunch. That 'bit' was a couple of hours of deep sleep. What a way to spend retirement, I thought, when will this pass? It did, some four months later.

Throughout my journey over four decades inside the NHS, like most other doctors, I gave lectures, seminars, and conference contributions to medical, nursing and other colleagues. Through my speciality of Community Child Health, I met and talked extensively with young people and parents in both the privacy of the clinic and public settings at school or playgroup. I have worked in the multicultural inner city and in rural settings, where I met the children of the titled and those of tied cottages. I played my part in service development – doing my share of time on national committees, serving as a British Medical Association (BMA) representative and spending a year on secondment at the Department of Health. People have repeatedly told me, 'Write – write a book.' I pondered over what sort of book might be written. There are already many telling the story of the foundation of the NHS or debating the direction the service is taking. Of course I have many friends who have also worked over a forty-year period inside the NHS, who also served on various committees. What makes my experience unique or special, why should I have a particular story to tell?

Perhaps this comes from my family. I was born into a family who, from their own experiences, were conscious of poverty, suffering and forced migration. My parents were active members of the Socialist Medical Association and throughout the 1930s they campaigned tirelessly for the NHS and gave unswervingly to the service. In 1998 this country celebrated fifty years of the NHS, proclaiming it as the first ever national health service. That was not true. The Soviet Union had launched theirs after the 1917 revolution. In 1938 my parents spent their honeymoon in the Soviet Union studying their health service, for health care was my father's passion. After the war, Dad was appointed Medical Officer of Health in a north London borough. We children accompanied him on his factory health inspections. I stared with fascination at the moving biscuits on the conveyor belt being covered with chocolate in Kemp's factory, I can recall the smell at Quink Ink and the cloth smells of Staples' Mattresses. With Dad, we swam with physically disabled children at special sessions at the public baths. At Christmas, Dad took us to the paper-chained day nurseries where my older brother and I entertained the children with our home-made papier mâché puppets and our childish shows.

Throughout the 1950s, my secondary school years were punctuated by family visits behind the Iron Curtain. I can clearly recall the delicate sound of the bell chimes in a sleep-therapy clinic in East Germany; the large and luscious peaches at the farm for the mentally ill in Hungary; the little decorated coat-pegs at the child-care centres in Poland. Dad was constantly writing books about health care: Mum was his collaborator. The stories of the health services became an integral part of our family life and experiences. Whilst I was doing my O-levels, there was wild excitement in our home when my parents' book *From Witchcraft to World Health* became a best seller and was published in several languages including Japanese, Finnish and Hungarian.

We really did believe that cooperation and planned development would eradicate poverty and disease. In the mid-50s Dad went with a British medical delegation to the Soviet Union. The doctors travelled to Tashkent. This was Dad's first and only trip outside Europe. From Tashkent, he wrote to us: 'It is heartrending to see how some people live without water, without sanitation, without light, but there is no doubt that there is a spirit and enthusiasm here that will overcome all obstacles.'

Then, the ascent of man seemed unstoppable. Today, life expectancy in Russia is falling. Tuberculosis and sexually transmitted diseases are on the increase in eastern Europe, as is lung cancer in young women who have taken up smoking. Social safeguards have disappeared and sickness in the main wage-earner shifts a whole family into impoverishment. Begging is rife. In sub-Saharan Africa we are witnessing a drastic increase in the illnesses we thought we could conquer – malaria and tuberculosis – together with the new, unforeseen horror of AIDS. Whilst British children suffer an epidemic of obesity, the numbers of the chronically hungry are increasing and the struggle for clean water has intensified. My mother has been dead for more than twenty years, my father for over forty. We do not live in the planned, health-enhancing cooperative world my parents had envisioned.

My story, however, is that of a woman doctor, a parent, working with other parents and children. What was it like to join the NHS at the close of its first decade? What did I discover about the place of mothers and children in society? Throughout those four decades of my working life, like all doctors, I constantly learned new modes of thinking, bringing a changing perspective and understanding. So here is the story of my journey, working with children, inside the NHS.

Chapter Two

Images From My Childhood

1948 In the playground of my primary school, I am playing chase with Evelyn, Edward and our other friends. The heavy, smelly machine is laying fresh tarmac on the roped-off part near the bomb shelters. As I joined the school after the war, we never actually use the shelters, but the older children tease us about going down into them. The war, with the continuing rationing, especially sweet rationing, still hangs over us. Our single-storey school building has a tall turret at one end where the infants' headmistress, Miss Townsend, sits. If you do well in class you are sent up the spiral stairs to receive a giant boiled sweet from a huge glass jar. 'Sweets from Australia,' she says, 'sent by our cousins over there.' As I really do have cousins over there, her comment puzzles me. It is an awesome experience to climb into the turret for my multicoloured gobstopper with its biting piece of aniseed at the core. Edward never goes up there.

Most of us schoolchildren wore the navy blue uniform with gold trim and a lovely badge that said '*Per Ardua ad Astra*' – by hard work to the stars. I had been well conditioned to believe that. Edward wore a grey jersey with bright red trim. He was a war orphan and wore the orphanage uniform. My parents constantly encouraged my hard work, I even had old scholarship papers to practise at home. My Dad had done 'intelligence tests' on me

5

from a very early age. Decades later when my mother died, I found amongst her collection of memorabilia a test paper on which my intellectual ability had been scored at age three years. This showed that I was able, even then, to say what a 'lecture' was. Edward, at age eleven, sat for those silent 90 minutes with the rest of us whilst we did the scholarship papers. He could neither read nor write, he just sat there playing with his pencil, smiling at me.

We knew that Edward could not read because during class we all had to read out loud in turn. We sat in rows with the cleverest children in the top row and the dunces in the bottom row. After end of term tests, we would change positions. There was always a scuffle to be top of the top row. I never was – there were two boys always ahead of me; both later made their mark in public life. My mother had schooled in Edinburgh and she told me that top of the top row was '*Dux*' and she had held that honour when she was ten. Class reading proceeded up and down the rows. We were so bored when the non-readers stammered through their paragraphs, but we cheered up when the reading gained speed half-way through the class. When I talked about these memories with one of my head-teacher colleagues in the late 1970s, he concurred that it had been just the same at his school in Wales, but with the top row sitting nearer to the coal fire whilst the dunces froze by the window.

Of course discipline was strict. We got marks every morning for tidy hair and polished shoes. I did badly in that. When there was misbehaviour generally in the class we all lined up regardless, and received two whacks with the ruler on the backs of our hands. As class monitor in my last year, I had to stand out in front of the forty-eight children in our class and write down the names of those who talked when the teacher was out of the room. Naturally, I overlooked my friends and wrote down the names of my enemies. Our headmaster was kindly but stern and distant. When chanting 'Our Father' in the big hall every morning, I thought we were talking to him. There was a picture on the wall in our top class which I now know was a print of Holbein's portrait of Henry VIII. I thought it was a picture of our strict and portly unmarried lady teacher. I was scared of her and also greatly admired her.

I never forgot Edward. My maternal grandparents lived with us, and I enjoyed a home filled with loving adults who were always there for us three children. My mother's social circle was mainly made up of her aunts, uncles and cousins. The regular Sunday teas with my paternal grandparents were an indulgence of goodies, the joy of meringues and games of hide and seek with my cousins around the treadle sewing machines in Grandpa's workroom. Young as I was, I felt a tremendous unfairness at Edward's plight. That sense stayed with me.

Leaving my primary school for a treasured scholarship place took me into a new world in the 1950s. Looking back, I remember my first school visit to a Children's Concert at the newly opened Royal Festival Hall. I thought I had entered a palace. I was overcome by the glamour of the 'ladies room' with the wash basins and illuminated mirrors, just like the film stars had. But even my grammar school seemed like a palace: the sparkling polished wooden floors, the huge hall with the rows of long light windows, the sound of the senior choir singing in the organ gallery, the lime avenue in the beautiful grounds and the magnificent cedar on the terrace. Of course it was a girls-only school. Our teachers were mainly unmarried – a cultural outcome of the marriage bar which was in force between the two world wars. Our teachers honoured learning and taught us about our privilege in being at this grammar school, and our duty to serve the wider community through our education and training.

We took our schooling seriously but we also had enormous fun, especially through the clubs available to us. I was never a sporty type, but I did enjoy the Polyglot Club, and the Drama and Debating Societies. I and my friends wrote for the school magazine from our early days, we sang in the senior choir and throughout those school years, we seemed to talk and argue about every subject under the sun! Even in the '50s we had the equivalent of a school council made up of elected form monitors. We took these elections seriously. I felt very honoured when, in my fifth form, I was voted class monitor along with my 'best enemy', Esther Rantzen. On reaching our school-leaving age of 18 years, our headmistress gave us a valedictory address in the Founders' Library. She advised us that at university there would be more boys than girls. This piece of information was followed by a significant pause. She was right, for in 1958 only one in four students was a woman and in medical school it was only one in eight … it really had been 'by hard work to the stars'. But oh how removed was our personal social education from present-day practice!

Such glimpses of an immediate post-war schooling conjure up consciousness of how vastly childhood and adolescence have been transformed during my working lifetime. Self-evidently, adult ideas about childhood in any historical period have never been fixed, but the changes in the past fifty years reflect truly dramatic shifts in expectations. How these changes percolated through to my training and professional life will be explored along this journey.

Chapter Three

Medical School

1958 Eight of us girls from our school went on to study medicine – a large quota from our sixth form. Of course I had never wanted to be a doctor. My parents had harboured that destiny for me, perhaps from the time of my three-year-old home tests. In the '50s, it was generally accepted that parents would talk to the head-teacher about the pupil's future without the individual being addressed at all. My 'career interview' with my headmistress was just five minutes before the dinner bell was due. She remarked that as I was going to be a doctor, the following four sciences would be my A-level programme. Before I could speak, the bell rang and I was dismissed. I spent the dinner hour at the bottom of our lime avenue, crying to my best friend that my whole life had been decided without my saying a word. In our generation you seldom had the chance to change careers. We all trained for a lifetime's dedication.

Arriving at medical school produced many strange encounters. The first and obvious one was having classes with the boys. At my girls' school we had led the debates, we ran the societies, acted lead roles of either sex in the plays and won the prizes. My Dad had tears of laughter running down his cheeks on seeing me, in correct uniform and oversized helmet, singing the part of the Sergeant of Police in *The Pirates of Penzance*. It was Grandpa who had hugged me so hard after watching me, bearded and in

9

a long black gown, play Shylock as the betrayed, suffering and misunderstood outsider. Now at university our confidence was challenged. The boys talked differently from us, seemed far cleverer than us and certainly ran the clubs, wrote the material for our 'Reviews' and directed the plays and shows in which we took part!

I also met students from the provincial towns. How different they seemed from us Londoners, which was not just a question of accents! At my primary school half the children had been Christian and half had been Jewish. My young self thought that was how it was everywhere. At my direct-grant grammar school a quota was enacted against the Jewish girls, with the admission rate fixed at one in six. Unsurprisingly, having been more highly selected, the Jewish girls did very well. The same quota was used by other direct-grant grammar schools across the area. This explains the abundance of Jewish children in the neighbouring county grammar schools, which could not enact a quota scheme. Among the 800 girls in my school there was one Indian girl.

One lunchtime, standing in the medical school cloakroom, Sarah asked me if I'd like to go to Hillel House for lunch. I agreed and so did Rosalind. One of our provincial girls asked if she could join us.

'It is a student place for Jewish students,' said Sarah.

'Are you Jewish?' gasped our provincial chum. As the penny dropped, she turned to look at the two of us, asking, 'And you? And you?' followed by, 'I've never seen a Jew before.'

By the 1950s, there had been a significant Jewish presence in Britain for at least three generations, derived from those fleeing the Tsarist Russian pogroms of the 1880s. My own maternal great-grandfather had fled from Lithuania and arrived alone in Edinburgh in 1883 – a lonely eighteen-year-old desperate refugee. My father's parents had arrived in East London from Poland a generation later, just before the Aliens Act closed the door to such asylum seekers. This exchange between us students, some fifty years later, was also ten years after Britain had been actively

10

recruiting from the West Indies and Indian subcontinent to make up our post-war labour shortage. If Jewish girls were an exotic rarity, what of the more recent newcomers?

I had joined my teaching hospital when the NHS was only ten years old. Our training was derived from the traditions experienced by those who trained us: our learning was formal, ordered and regularly tested. I never remember any medical teacher discussing the fact that we had an NHS or ever debating its structure or significance. The sense of pride and professional identity evident amongst our consultants derived from belonging to a well-respected London teaching hospital with its established tradition and flourishing private wing. That tradition included a formality in dress and manners. One of my pals received a note in his pigeon-hole to the effect that young men who sported beards did not advance in the department.

Students were indeed relegated to the lowest position in the pecking order. It was not uncommon for our teachers to mock or humiliate us. I remember standing on a box to hold the retractor for a long period while my surgeon worked away deep in the patient's belly. I could not see a thing, my arm began to ache and I was really scared to loosen the tension of my hold. I had been selected for this task because, the surgeon declared, I had marched from Aldermaston to 'Ban the Bomb', so I must have the strength for this job. (I wondered how he knew.) It was the regular dissimulation of information from patients behind a screen of Latin which elevated the doctor's position. The modern idea of partnership with patients or patient helplines was worlds away from the ethos of my training. Hospitals were run for the consultants, with ward sisters ensuring that everything was in exact order before the ward round. It was only when I was on a post-graduate course that a consultant, caring for the elderly, asked us to imagine how people had received their care before the NHS existed. This so startled me that later I always put the same question to young students when it was my turn to train others.

We medical students would progress from 'firm' to 'firm' to witness the work of the various specialities. Unusual cases were demonstrated at the 'circus' where we did indeed sit in tiered rows rising above the floor-space where the training doctor would display the key features of his interesting patient. We would interpose our questions about the condition. We were encouraged to attend post-mortems, especially those of the deceased patients whom we ourselves had 'clerked'. That was a really testing experience for us novices. You had to work hard at showing a professional, detached interest. Today this practice has been overtaken by the ability to visualise what has gone wrong inside, with cross-section body scanning.

For the students, general surgery and general medicine were the major draws. Public Health had such a low profile that only some half dozen of us attended the lectures. When we turned up at the venereal diseases clinic we were asked why we had come, as it was nearly all over thanks to penicillin. We were told that we should go to the pictures instead ... which, being cinema addicts, we duly did!

One of our options was to attend the sessions run by Dr Michael Balint, the psychoanalyst who wrote about the patient, the doctor and the illness. A group of us friends used to do the weekly walk of a mile over to his place. He asked us, in turn, to present a patient whom we were currently looking after. His angle was not so much to talk about the medical condition as the actual person. He would begin to ask querulous questions to make us think of patient-centred medicine. We experienced uncertainty. His enquiries would become more penetrating and he would smile almost playfully at us as we searched for appropriate responses. He was making us think why that patient had the illness at that particular time. We were encouraged to consider how the illness affected the patient's personality, sexual life, work and nearest relatives. This humanised our consideration of the impact of disease. We found those weekly seminars highly stimulating. Of that group of my friends, several became psychiatrists, whilst two of us went into community child health work. In her mature years, one friend found her niche doing sterling work for the Medical Foundation for the Care of Victims of Torture. Founded in 1985 this organisation has helped over 40,000 survivors from many different countries.

The years at medical school never dragged. We only had long summer breaks in the first two academic years. Once we moved onto the wards we seemed to be timetabled throughout the three years, passing from firm to firm. We still kept up singing and acting in Medical School Reviews. Certainly we haunted the cinemas. We had a monthly discussion society where invited speakers addressed topics of general political or cultural interest. We would host the speaker at the Chinese restaurant belonging to the uncle of one of our committee members. I served on that committee as the statutory female.

One of my last placements was in the infectious diseases hospital miles away in south London. There I developed acute appendicitis. A women medic who ran a battered old van kindly drove me back to my parents' home, but what a drive that was! We phoned my brother who was doing his post-graduate resident surgical job.

'What's the registrar on duty like?' I asked.

'Oh he's OK. Why?'

''Cos I'm coming in with appendicitis.'

Even after the sedation, I was laughing as my brother and one of his friends sat and joked at my bedside. This was just before my part-one finals in pathology. The Dean wrote a kind letter offering six months' deferral, but I replied saying I would attend. We were examined by our own hospital staff. Placing a specimen pot with an inflamed appendix on the table, my teacher asked, 'And what is that please?'

I immediately replied, 'Mine!'

I do not recall training in family planning during our student years, although we worked in the gynaecology department. The experience that really came alive was our three months in the

Maternity Unit. This seems a good place to let my story take off, as the issues of childbearing, family planning and abortion were simmering when I was a student and were soon to spill over into the public arena in the Swinging Sixties. However, before I move on to the obstetric ward, let us see why I was eligible to be standing on the box in the surgical theatre ... why we had joined the Aldermaston Marches.

Chapter Four

It's a Long Way to Limp to London!

More than a dozen years passed between the dropping of the atom bomb on Hiroshima and the formation of the Campaign for Nuclear Disarmament (CND) in 1958. I was then in my last year at secondary school. The Russians had been told about the successful first atomic bomb explosion at Los Alamos, the new and terrible bomb capable of destroying a whole city. That August in 1945, the Russian military were invited to see the ruins of Hiroshima and Nagasaki. Subsequently, the American occupation force imposed the Press Code and confiscated photographs, films, poems, novels about the bomb, suppressing scientific studies and medical records. The terrible impact of the bombings were thus concealed from the world's public, indeed even from the Japanese outside those two cities. It was actually illegal for Japanese doctors to conduct medical studies on the effects of the A-bomb, whilst writers and journalists were largely prevented from publishing information about the desperate plight of survivors. Secrecy was not only confined to events in Japan but also surrounded the British government's decision to build a British bomb. Western scientists, clergy and pacifists, growing aware of the nuclear arms race, and prompted by the hydrogen bomb detonations, held conferences and public actions to oppose the further development of nuclear weapons. However, it took those dozen years before a grass-roots protest movement was organised. This movement germinated in my parents' home.

15

I well remember the day the CND symbol, designed by the local ceramics potter Eric Austen, was brought to our house for the first time. Being an active Girl Guide, I quickly recognised the way the semaphore positions for *N* and *D* had been cleverly incorporated within the compulsory traffic symbol of the circle. The original design had shaped bases for the diagonals so the image resembled a rocket on its launch pad.

How was it that this took place in my family home? Back in the 1930s my mother's search for a group of politically active women had brought her into the Women's Cooperative Guild. She found herself well in sympathy with their pacifist ideas and their tradition of wearing white peace poppies on Remembrance Sunday. The rise of fascism, however, produced friction over this pacifist policy and the Spanish Civil War became the focus for dissent. The Kentish Town Branch had denounced non-intervention, calling for arms to fight fascism. My mother, a member of the neighbouring Holloway Branch, came up with a compromise gesture which became adopted by all Cooperative Stores – the sale of cardboard milk tokens to raise money for the child victims of the war. During the Second World War, its pacifism lost the Guild nearly a third of its members. Yet following the ending of American censorship in Japan in 1953, it was a Guild branch which gave voice to the outcry against nuclear weapons.

The horror of the Bikini tests, with the island blown apart (hence the name 'bikini' was used for the scanty two-piece swimsuit) and the radioactive fallout extending beyond the exclusion zone fatally contaminating the Japanese fishing boat *Lucky Dragon*, had been discussed by the women in the Golders Green Guild Branch. Street petitions had been presented to shoppers, branch members had attended the London Cooperative Education Department conference on the H-bomb, and the white poppy continued to be worn.

Then Dad brought home the medical paper reporting the rise in childhood leukaemia and malformed children years after the mothers' exposure to radiation, as a result of genetic effects. He

16

talked about it over supper. The next Wednesday, Mum went to her Guild afternoon and told her friends about the technical paper. She thought it sounded coldly scientific and distant, but in the little meeting room attached to a local church, the effect was explosive. Voices were raised about '*doing something*'. A tall, thin, rather melancholy-looking woman, whom Mum had not seen at the Guild before, stood up saying, 'I don't often come to the Guild but I'm very glad I came today.' That was how Mum and Miss Fishwick ('G.F. Fishwick, you can call me Jeff,' she said shyly) got together in our kitchen to work on their campaign.

Miss Fishwick was a retired civil servant, a member of the Finchley Labour Party and the Anglican Pacifist Fellowship and had been a suffragette. Many suffragettes remained active right up to their declining years – the veteran suffragette Mary Leigh was on the first Aldermaston March at age 73. Mum and Jeff proved to be a good two-woman team. Mum could find the contacts in the local trades union groups and other organisations, Jeff would go on her bicycle and visit the local churchmen. Mum would draw up the letters and circulars, Jeff would vet them with civil service precision, often telephoning early in the morning before Mum was out of bed.

'I think that should be a semicolon not a full stop,' she would say.

Dad, pulling on his trousers, grumbled, 'Doesn't that woman ever give you peace?'

From such kitchen politics, the campaign grew. Uniting around the issue that would draw the widest support, Mum grumbled that she had to agree to the impossibly unattractive title of the Local Committee for the Abolition of Nuclear Weapons Tests (LCANWT). The committee was particularly enhanced when the Quaker proprietor of the *Hampstead and Highgate Gazette*, Arthur Goss, threw his energies and the valuable support of his paper behind the cause. We teenagers grew used to holding posters, petitioning in the streets on Saturday afternoons and going to

17

informative meetings. What was needed now was something more than posters, headlines, brains trusts and petitions – something that would really capture the imagination and move people. The Guild found that something by giving space to voices from Japan.

Following the end of the American occupation, Japanese people began to travel abroad, bearing witness to the hellish experience of atomic bombing. Since the '30s, my Dad had been an activist in the Socialist Medical Association, which was sponsoring the visit of four Japanese women to Britain. Thus it was that in April 1955, when I was fifteen years old, I heard Kikue Ihara, a teacher from Nagasaki, address the Golders Green Branch Guild, describing the horror experienced by her schoolchildren. One boy from her class had cried to her from his hospital bed, 'Why didn't you tell us about the burning sun?' Now, she declared, she would devote her life to telling the whole world about the burning sun. Her gentle but firm words carried a terrific impact. She handed round a tile with a shadow of a hand on it; the hand of someone who had just vaporised in that horrendous heat. It was impossible not to be shaken and moved.

With the ending of censorship, the Japanese Teachers Union determined to make a film using a script compiled by Arata Nagata, Professor of Hiroshima University, based on essays by Hiroshima schoolchildren. Shindo Kaneto was commissioned to make the film *Children of the Atom Bomb*. Filmed on location, it was released on 6th August 1952 to commemorate Hiroshima Memorial Day. Kaneto himself did not experience the bombing but, coming from Hiroshima, he felt close to the subject. Jeff heard of this film; the Guild decided to screen it.

Mum made the usual arrangements, booking the hall and organising publicity. Then Jeff announced that the 'Hiroshima Panels', painted by two Japanese artists Iri and Toshi Maruki, were currently with Sir Richard Ackland. Not really expecting a reply, Mum sent off a letter. On the morning of the screening, whilst we were at the hall doing the usual search for appropriate electric plugs, worrying whether the film projector would work

18

and was the screen big enough, and all the dozens of other things that meeting organisers have nightmares about, the caretaker announced that a van with the six large panels had arrived! With a great struggle, and the help of a passer-by, these were unloaded and fixed around the walls of the hall. We all stood back, stunned by the effect. The black and white images portrayed a continuous stream of burning, naked, dying people struggling away from that city engulfed by the explosion of a single A-bomb, towards a great river. That evening the hall was packed. Anyone who saw *Children of Hiroshima* must still remember the tragic effect of the soundtrack. In Western cinema, chaos is evinced by cacophony and discordant music but this was not music, it was not a devastating noise. There was a profoundly deep, humming, single note during which children were seen exercising in a school playground, then a held, ominous silence, followed by the explosion.

Inspired by the Japanese teacher and using visual imagery in painting and film, this modest group of Guildswomen with their pacifist tradition did stir public imagination. Parallel LCANWTs rapidly emerged across the country, merging in 1958 to form CND. Thus it was that when we were in the sixth form at school, I and my friends from our own and other local schools felt we simply had to join the first Aldermaston March. We made our own, highly amateurish banner which, to our great pride, appeared on the front page of the *Sunday Observer*. Together with the other young people we sang *Don't you hear the H bomb's thunder, echo like the crack of doom*, chanted *Ban the Bomb for evermore* and waved our banner. To our blistered feet, we sang *It's a long way to limp to London*. Three of our male friends, walking with arms around each other's necks, were scolded by an organising steward: 'You three look sloppy.' The father of one of my girl friends held a senior position in the military. He stood on the corner of Parliament Square and, as we limped by, he shouted 'Well done you girls!' That first march had a much reduced following on days two and three. Our arrival on the fourth day at Aldermaston, the weapons research establishment, felt somewhat of an anticlimax. Next time we had to do better than that.

Miss Fishwick went on tirelessly campaigning, an aged woman riding around on her bike to meetings and petitioning people. She was ill with flu that next winter and died before she could know of the astounding success of the second march. It was Easter 1959, I was a first-year medical student, and we marched with the university group from Aldermaston over the four days to London. One of our dental friends was with us – he was very funny. He and my brother had collaborated with other friends to write the material for our medical student reviews and many of the sketches were very sardonic. We hadn't made it to the Edinburgh Footlights but we were selected for a charity show in a Shaftesbury Avenue theatre. The Duke of Edinburgh sat in his box in the audience, as we sang and danced our calypso 'Cuba Sugar' about the revolution in that island. Our dental pal walked with us on that Aldermaston March, reading a novel all the way. Our arrival at Trafalgar Square, overflowing with 100,000 people, was an exhilarating sensation, wiping out the discomforts and arguments about the value of the previous four days' march.

What had been the real value of our marches? The Cold War continued and intensified. We were in our fifth and final year of medical studies in the autumn of the Cuban missile crisis. Four of us students, including our dental friend, were sharing digs. He posted a notice on the door saying 'Goodbye'; we sat on the floor and dealt out four hands for canasta. We played cards till Krushchev ordered the Soviet ships to turn around.

On those Aldermaston Marches we had slept the nights on the floors of community halls. I remember with great poignancy how, at one of the halls, two violinists had come to play an extract from Bach's Double Violin Concerto. We seemed to live in a mad, mad world. We were fearful for the future. Was there any point in getting married and having kids if that was the sort of world we lived in? My older brother had been born as fascism intensified. My sister and I were both war babies. What had my

parents felt? Yes, love – making love and producing children –
went on as usual, as I was soon to learn in my time on the
obstetric wards.

Chapter Five

Childbirth: The Future Starts Here

Our Professor of Obstetrics, W.C.W. Nixon, was a remarkable teacher. On previous firms we had become accustomed to taking medical histories from the patients, making careful examinations, eliciting significant signs. We hung on the consultant's words during ward rounds and were careful to keep out of the way and never intrude. Professor Nixon aimed to involve us in making childbirth a great experience for the mothers and their husbands. In a novel manner for the beginning of the 1960s, fathers were encouraged to attend classes and be present at the birth. We were encouraged to feel that even medical students were part of a team. Our ideas were sought on how the department was run, on the teaching plan, on how we could increase our own contribution. I wrote proposing a scheme that would give us greater practical experience than just attending normal births. This was met by the registrar allowing my assistance at a forceps delivery – his hands over mine as I pulled on the forceps! He later announced at the team meeting that he liked to deal with disgruntled students first. But this was not a romanticised department. The burden of unwanted pregnancies was addressed and we learned about the sickness and deaths that accompanied illegal abortions. Professor Nixon was outspoken in public debate, for abortions were only permitted when there was significant threat to the life and health of the mother.

On the maternity wards we were exposed to an intimacy of contact which felt quite new. We saw first-hand the concerns our chief had raised. We sat with teenage, unmarried girls who had been rejected by their families and were alone in labour. We sat with mothers who thought they had completed their families, yet, with teenagers already at home, were expecting again. We went out with the district midwives and saw mothers in their own homes, many in council flats, which was a revelation for us greenhorns. Like myself, the majority of London medical students were themselves the children of doctors. Most importantly, we felt the historic divide between the experienced, all-female midwives and the force of the male obstetricians. I remember one woman giving birth to a breech presentation and, in great distress, cursing and crying out. She clutched at me violently, tearing my shirt. Scolded by her male obstetrician, she yelled, 'Jesus, you should be having this!'

He retorted, 'It's not me, nor ever will be. It's you, so shut up and do what you are told.'

Can obstetricians talk like that now? Today over half of new medical students are women and obstetrics is popular with women doctors. Male obstetricians now find that it is they who are in the position of being the 'statutory male' on their specialist committees.

Following my graduation, it was compulsory to live in for the first year. I spent the first six months in my teaching hospital and then applied for a surgical house job, which included ten gynaecology beds, for the second six months. What a revelation it was just to move some five miles up the road to a non-teaching hospital. During my undergraduate experience the ward sisters had been well-spoken, calmly efficient and fairly remote from us students. Several had double-barrelled names, some had been debutantes. All were English. Up the road I met friendly Irish sisters, who became good chums and a power of support to us inexperienced doctors. I met my first black nurses – one was the night sister. Six years later, back in my teaching hospital maternity ward giving birth to our own first child, it was black sisters who cared for me.

At my surgical house job interview I had been asked whether I was pregnant. I was not. I later learned that the previous woman doctor had been expecting and had had much time off with sick leave. This question was not asked of a fellow woman doctor applying for a parallel post at the same time as myself. She got her job and was pregnant. It all seemed random and felt intrusive. It was the unwanted pregnancies that dominated the next six months. Week after week brought a toll of suffering girls and women. Many had been for back-street abortions, had started to bleed and came to us hoping the loss would be inevitable. I will never forget one lovely-looking student who, being pregnant, had jumped from a first-floor window. She had landed on her side, with a bush breaking her fall. She broke bone after bone on her left side but did not abort. It was whilst she was in traction in one of our beds that she finally miscarried.

Sister was wonderful with these sad women. I learned a lot from her and worked at talking with all our patients. There was one girl who lay silent and refused to speak to any of us staff. We found out from other patients that she had come to London from the north to seek an abortion. Whoever she had visited had started her off, stolen her handbag, and left her bleeding heavily at our casualty entrance. The other patients had a whip-round to help her before she left our hospital.

It was always stressful when we went to theatre. My job was to scrape the womb to empty it, but to be careful not to do any damage. It seemed a terrible responsibility. During those six months, I estimated that I completed over one hundred abortions. We never actually lost a woman, but women were dying from illegal abortions and most of these women were already mothers. There had to be another way. I discovered the Abortion Law Reform Association, which was painstakingly collecting statistics about deaths and damage to support the campaign for change. There were an estimated 100,000 illegal abortions every year. During parliamentary debate Lord Silkin referred to the trail of diseases, haemorrhages and displacements following unskilled interventions, stating this was as much a human sacrifice as the death toll itself. Whilst opinion polls showed that most families wanted two to three children, and over 70% of married couples approved of birth control, family-planning advice was mainly available through the voluntary sector not the NHS. Eminent doctors were pressing for contraception and sterilisation to be offered on the NHS. Sir Dugald Baird in Aberdeen already ran such a service. Professor Nixon never lived to see parliamentary reform – he died in 1966. The edition of the *British Medical Journal* carrying his obituary also published his last letter arguing for relief for families in poverty by providing the Fifth Freedom: freedom from unwanted pregnancies.

One of my visits as a student was to a mum in the local council flats, who was booked for a home delivery with the midwife. In that period we used X-rays to check the baby's head against pelvis size. Today expectant mums have their own copies of pictures, taken with ultrasound technology, of the growing baby inside their womb. These clearly show the size of the baby relative to the size of the mother's pelvis. Our mum in her overcrowded flat, already had three boys aged between seventeen years and twenty months. Her husband had prepared hot water, cloth handkerchiefs and tea. The mother's labour went into 'distress'. The midwife, recognising disproportion, called for the Flying Squad – our mobile emergency ambulance team. Terrified at her transfer to hospital, this mother gripped my hand, begging me not to leave her. In theatre our obstetrician regarded the anaesthetised woman and announced, 'Now, Miss Leff, look at those monstrous contractions. If we do nothing, the womb will rupture and we will lose both mother and baby.' With great skill he managed a forceps delivery. As our patient was wheeled back to the ward, I grabbed her hand and, as she came to, I had the privilege of telling her she had a healthy baby girl.

This experience made me wonder what had happened to women in obstructed labour before the forceps were invented.

This had not been discussed in our lectures. I searched the library and found out about Jacob Nufer, a sow herdsman who lived near Lake Constance. Around 1500, he did a caesarian section on his wife who was struggling in such a labour. His is thought to be the first recorded section where both mother and baby survived. I thought of how he must have gained experience with his sows, but what desperation and courage must have driven him to cut open his own wife. I then read how later in the sixteenth century, a family of Huguenot descent living in southern England had invented the forceps. By this invention Peter Chamberlen saved women from the existing practice of piecemeal removal of babies who could not pass through the birth canal. But what did Chamberlen do with his invention? He and his descendants kept it a secret for 125 years, so that the family benefited from their reputation for safe deliveries in difficult births. When the secret was sold to a Dutch doctor, a single blade only was provided, which was useless. I was horrified by this story. What type of attitude allowed such exploitation? How could men be so self-seeking and knowingly leave unassisted women to die in horrible suffering? Did they have no conscience?

Apart from death during obstructed births, there had also been death from infection at childbirth (child-bed fever). Before the era of television cooks, innumerable households relied on the famous Mrs Beeton's book on household management, written in the mid-nineteenth century. We certainly used her recipes in my family home. However, all her expert knowledge and advice on home cleanliness and domestic management could not save Isabella Beeton herself, who died of child-bed fever aged twenty-nine, after the birth of her fourth son. Dr Semmelweiss, who died in 1865, the same year as Mrs Beeton, had known the answer. He was a Hungarian doctor who noted that an assistant had died of a fever mimicking child-bed fever after doing a post-mortem on a dead mother. He realised that women were more likely to fall ill when delivered by medical students who had come from the dissection room, than if delivered by midwives.

He gave out the edict 'Wash Your Hands' and the death rate in his hospital fell tenfold. However, his work was not accepted and his knowledge could not save Mrs Beeton. The opposition he experienced drove him insane and he died in an asylum, aged fifty. Semmelweiss is now honoured and his home in Budapest is a memorial museum. I was very moved when, in my fifties, I made a visit there.

Why was it that advances to help women in this natural, and then barely avoidable, experience of child bearing, were so resisted? Even when the anaesthetic power of chloroform was accidentally discovered by James Simpson in 1840, the priests spoke out against its use – declaring that pain in childbirth helped women to turn to God. The Curse of Eve was a cultural reality. It was Queen Victoria who settled that argument. She well knew what childbirth entailed and used chloroform at the birth of her seventh child, Prince Leopold.

Those months in the Obstetric Unit taught me that technological advance alone cannot improve the experience of childbirth: change in attitude is also important. Of course expediency has always played a part in service plans. When I and my friends had our children in the 1960s, we were strongly advised to have the first in hospital and to remain there until the baby was ten days old. If the birth was normal, the second would have to be delivered at home due to pressure on beds. I went to the homes of several of my women friends to be with them at their second births.

Today women are invited to discuss their preferences about delivery. Women can choose 'labour partners' to give support during birth. Water-births may be used in place of anaesthesia and can even be organised at home. It has been a long journey to increase the joy of such an important event. I remember seeing my first film of childbirth while I was a student. We were told that having found a mother who agreed to take part, the first film was ruined. The cameramen, who had never seen a birth before, were so moved that their own tears as the baby was born stopped their filming. Yes, bringing new life into the world is a great adventure ... and every child should be a wanted child!

Chapter Six

'Every Child A Wanted Child'

This was the powerful slogan of the 1960s. For the slogan to be the reality, we needed effective contraception, education and a provider service. Having spent six months finishing off those illegal abortions, I wanted to know why contraceptive advice was not part of routine care. Why had such widespread ignorance and lack of services persisted, well into the second decade of the NHS? We had not even learned family-planning techniques as medical students, so here was another topic for me to explore in the library!

Of course, throughout most of recorded time, it was not family limitation but the struggle for survival which was the significant issue. War, famine and disease were the great decimators of populations, and in many parts of the world, remain so today. When, at the end of the eighteenth century, Thomas Malthus published his significant essay on the pressure of the increasing population on food production, his solution was for people either to be completely celibate or to arrange late marriages. Biology was indeed destiny. Childbearing started soon after puberty, and women would commonly rear large families of six to twelve children. Many of the children died in infancy and childhood of the common infectious diseases. Many women, succumbing to child-bed and other fevers, never lived to see their children grow up. Most women's lives were thus completely taken up with pregnancy and child rearing: there was no 'empty nest' syndrome for them. My own great-grandmother, living in Edinburgh at the end of the nineteenth century, had no choice but to bear her eight children, of whom my grandfather was the eldest.

Four generations later, it still remained difficult for women to train as doctors. In 1958 I had been turned down at several London teaching hospitals before I secured an offer of a place. At one interview, without lifting their heads, the doctors poring over my application form asked me what position I played on the rugby field! I did an 'ahem' and mumbled about not having played rugby. At the medical school where my father had trained, I was asked if I had any personal connection with the school. I named my father and was promptly rejected. My brother was already training at the school which finally accepted me, so perhaps family connections do help! I felt lucky to have got a medical student place. I knew that it was only after a fierce struggle that the first medical school for women had opened in London in 1874. The first women doctors chose to work with women and children. Dr Elizabeth Blackwell worked with women with syphilis in the almshouses of Philadelphia. Dr Annie McCall ran a maternity hospital in Clapham, advocating explicit teaching in a deeply friendly manner as a means of 'rescuing' women in pregnancy and childbirth. Dr Elizabeth Garrett Anderson, Britain's first woman doctor, was an advocate for both marriage and a career. Educated women were also challenging the sexual double standard which approved sexual adventuring for young gentlemen, whilst their sisters were kept in modest ignorance. The accepted form advised these girls to 'suffer and be still'. No wonder attacks of hysterics were frequently endured by the young ladies of the family! Women doctors argued that women's health would never be properly cared for until the care was provided by women. What would those Victorian women have thought of my 'through the glass ceiling' Government programme?

In the mid-60s when I was appointed to the Camden Town clinic, the sexual double standard was alive and well. At our clinic

I met girls who were 'in trouble', but I never heard of any boys or men in the same state. Within my catchment area there were two Mother and Baby Homes for these girls, one Catholic and the other Church of England. The voluntary body which offered assistance had the stigmatising name The Council for the Unmarried Mother and her Child. Their headquarters were just up the road in Kentish Town. My job was to carry out ante-natal examinations at the clinic in between the girls' visits to the maternity hospital. After their babies were born, I met the girls again for post-natal checks. I did this work before I had children of my own, which strongly limited my comprehension of what those girls must have suffered. They did talk at our clinic – mostly they complained bitterly about the cruel humiliations they were subjected to. Punishment for sexual sinning appeared to have been part of the ethos of the Homes. One girl cried how, heavily pregnant, she had had to go down on her hands and knees to polish the brass fender in the common room. Another was scolded for taking too thick a peel off the potatoes. She was made to take the peelings from the bin to scrape off more for the cooking pot. It is only recently that similar stories of this period have been aired through popular novels and films.

The worst practice of all was the rule that the girls should keep and nurse their babies for six weeks before the infants were placed for adoption. It does give the babies a better start to be breast fed at the outset, and breast feeding does help the woman's body return to the non-pregnant state, but what emotional turmoil these girls must have experienced! At their six-week post-natal check, just before they separated from their children, the girls were subdued. I am struck by how far removed this policy was from today's more humane response of open adoption, where birth mothers may keep in touch with adoptive mothers and receive news of the child's progress. Thankfully I was working just at the tail-end of the old practice, which changed when the stigma of being a single mother changed and girls without partners began to be supported by their own parents.

I was intrigued to observe that parliament passed the Act making abortion more widely available in 1967, one year before family planning was accepted as an NHS provision. The open fight for contraceptive advice really did stretch back nearly one hundred years. In my library search, I read about Charles Bradlaugh, MP, who together with the social reformer Annie Besant in 1877 re-issued the banned birth control pamphlet entitled *The Fruits of Philosophy*. Mrs Besant declared that she was moved by a higher sense of morality yet, as a divorcee, she knew she was risking her reputation. She also feared possible public scorn and damage to Bradlaugh's political career. The pair were indeed indicted for producing a lewd, bawdy and obscene publication, expounding the freakish ideas of the free-love class of persons. Were the Victorians right to have feared that the control of conception would give rise to the widespread practice of sex whenever and with whomever? Although Bradlaugh and Mrs Besant were found guilty, the conviction was set aside at appeal because of a legal defect. Mrs Besant continued to address public meetings and was inundated with hundreds of letters from poor married women seeking advice.

Into this rage against sexual double standards, inequalities and ignorance stirring up the London scene, came twenty-six-year-old Dr Aletta Jacobs, the first woman doctor to have qualified in Holland. She met Bradlaugh and Besant at a meeting of the Malthusian Society and became convinced of the woman's right to choose to have children. Jacobs visited Elizabeth Garrett Anderson's hospital and, meeting her sister Millicent Garrett Fawcett, learned of the women's suffrage campaign. Returning to Holland, Jacobs pioneered the contraceptive pessary (the Dutch cap). She unsuccessfully challenged the Mayor of Amsterdam to place her name on the electoral roll. It was argued that only with female suffrage would women's needs be truly addressed. Yet suffrage came many decades before effective, available contraception.

Before the 1968 Act was passed, we were able to give contraceptive advice to women who, on health grounds, should wait before a further pregnancy. Most of our patients were the mothers whom we had met in the ante-natal clinic or our child health clinics. It was approved practice in our borough that any woman in overcrowded accommodation or with a child under two years should have free advice. Thus we were able to help all the women who applied to us. We ran an evening family-planning clinic to help working mothers or those who needed to leave their babies with their husbands while they attended. Even so, some of the women had problems with their partners' attitudes. One told me how her partner kept her Dutch cap in a locked cupboard and when he wanted sex, he would throw the key at her. Another told how her jealous husband had stabbed multiple punctures into her Dutch cap. Women really needed a contraceptive method over which they themselves had full control. All our women were married, or declared themselves to be married. What struck us most about the 1968 Act was that advice was to be available to all who needed it, whether married or unmarried, over the age of consent.

We next got into difficult situations with those who lied about being sixteen. Those who openly declared their under-age status were referred to the Brook Advisory Centre which ran a specialist service for such young people. This issue was not really resolved for a further sixteen years, when the Gillick case ruling advised that clinical decisions should be made relative to the maturity of the young person. Today the issue is not contraceptive advice, but whether the person under sixteen has the right to privacy when she requests a termination. The recent ruling is that while it is not essential to inform the parents, the young person should be encouraged to enlist the support of a responsible adult.

It could be argued that the Swinging Sixties started on 10th May 1960, the day that the American Food and Drug Agency licensed the contraceptive pill. Through the late '50s this had been used with Puerto Rican women and follow-up studies appeared, not accurately as it turned out, to show that it was effective and seemingly safe. By the time we opened the doors of our NHS clinics to all, whether married or unmarried, we could offer the cap, the pill or the coil which was inserted inside the womb. But while we were expanding our contraceptive service, the legal abortion rate was also taking off. Within five years of abortion law reform the annual rate of legal abortions topped the 100,000 mark, which had been the estimate before legalisation.

In the 1970s the Women's Liberation Movement began to demand self-control for women over their own bodies and reproductive functions. Women began to practise self-examination of the neck of the womb with mirrors. Today hospitals are using trained lay women to teach pelvic examination of women to medical students. Trials show that students learn better from lay women teachers than through traditional methods. Despite all this progress in methods, education and service provision, the need for an abortion service has hardly withered away. Britain has the highest rate of teenage mothers compared with other European countries. But then, sexual intimacy is about passion – and passion was never known to rely on reason.

Chapter Seven

Breaking the Mould of Institutional Care

I met Dr DeLargy when I was studying on the post-graduate course in Public Health in the mid-60s. It was he who had asked how people had obtained medical help before the NHS was founded. He described his London geriatric hospital at the beginning of the NHS. The building was an old workhouse, complete with chapel and organ, and heated by numerous coal fires. There were over 1000 cot beds in the dormitories arranged closely packed together, side by side in long rows. To examine a patient, the neighbouring cot bed had to be pulled out of line to allow access to the patient's bedside. The hospital was regarded as the dustbin of the teaching hospitals and of GPs. The only vacancy was a death vacancy. The GP's admission letter would read: 'Mr S, suffering from senility. Please dispose.' Ward sisters aimed to keep patients heavily sedated and quietly in bed. The activity on the doctor's ward round was the signing of death certificates.

It took years of hard work, re-educating staff, public and management, to transform this culture by cutting bed numbers and re-structuring wards as small social units, with the active engagement of social workers and community nurses in planned after-care. This pattern was repeated with other vulnerable groups, as we saw in our disturbing public health visit to the common lodging house provided for alcoholics, 'men without a settled way of life'. We walked through depressing dormitories with monstrous rows of black iron bedsteads. Hundreds used the lodging house – the offices held case notes on thousands. But we also learned about the new rehabilitation hostels, where small numbers of men were being reintegrated into society. Such developments would have been impossible without the NHS.

However, this story is about the children. When Edward was my young friend I never visited his orphanage, but as a children's doctor in the community in the mid-70s, I was attached to a children's home. Thankfully the children wore the uniforms of the various schools they attended. The dormitories, however, had long lines of beds, each bed with ugly black iron at head and foot. Beside each was a small locker for some few personal items. The spacious common room had settees, soft chairs and a TV. The children ate in a large dining room. The home was run by a husband and wife team living on the premises, but the stigma of institution pervaded the place.

During my Public Health training in the mid-60s, I had a placement in York and there I saw a bold improvement in child care. At the end of a cul-de-sac lined by semi-detached houses, the last semi-detached pair had been adapted to be a care home for a small group of ten children. Bedrooms were shared by just two or three children. There were various small rooms downstairs used for mealtimes, for relaxation and as a home-work room. Whilst there was a lead male and lead female carer, the staff were resident on a rotational basis. The children could play out in the cul-de-sac with others who lived in the street. This appeared to be a humanising approach, but it was still a far cry from the present policy of aiming to place all children in foster families.

It wasn't just child care in the community which was institutionalised, but also child care inside the hospitals. Whilst the structure of buildings create part of the culture, attitudes are even more important. After my registration year, I chose to do residential work in the children's hospitals. In the early '60s parental visiting was then strictly limited to a couple of hour slots and it was quite exceptional for parents to be allowed to sleep in alongside their sick children. There was a public campaign under way for parents to be able to stay with their children. My paediatric consultant, Dr Yudkin, was extremely supportive. We had a camp bed and some mothers did stay. Such mothers tended their children in a manner we could never match. I recall one young girl with meningitis. We had been asked to encourage her to drink. Her mother stayed whole days and nights with her daughter and meticulously offered drinks, measuring and charting the amounts taken. The child fully recovered. Most other children were visited only at visiting times. I was unsure whether parents had other pressures, were inhibited by the rules, or even felt intimidated at the thought of sleeping in the children's ward. Some ten years later, when my own sick son was admitted to hospital, I was without question able to remain by his bedside throughout his several days of admission.

I remember well our work on the baby ward. We had a wide-mouthed bucket in the middle of the floor to catch rainwater from the leaking roof. This ward was not directly under the roof, but under the ward that was under the roof!

I was incensed and wrote to Kenneth Robinson, who in 1964 was both Minister for Health and my local MP. His reply anticipated the story of the rest of my time in the NHS. He advised that we could not afford to put more into the Health Service until we had solved Britain's economic problems. His tone then softened and, naming my late father and remembering his work for the NHS, he asked whether I was a relation.

I blush when I think back to that baby ward. Many evenings on duty, when not required for actual work on the wards, I still had to be available 'on call'. I had made friends with several nurses, and Sister on the baby ward was a particular favourite of mine. I would go up there and sit and chat with her of an evening and during this time we would both bottle feed the sick babies. We would talk away, noting the amount drunk and winding the babies but they were almost 'objects' to us. A nurse would call out, 'Have you done cot five?' and a baby and bottle would be passed to us. It was not until I had my own children that I remembered with embarrassment our attitudes then. Throughout my working life, I have always maintained that I learned more through having my own children than from any lectures or courses I attended.

Whilst I was working at the Camden Town clinic, we had a push to encourage breast feeding. Many of our community nurses were unmarried and without children of their own. I was breast feeding our first child. Dr Harding, our Medical Officer of Health asked me whether I would attend a breast-feeding support day and speak to the nurses about my experience. Naturally, I agreed. I stood at the microphone and told the packed hall that before becoming a mother myself, I had never really understood the fatigue effect of feeding. I had thought I was an old hand, as I estimated that I had professionally handled some 500 babies before holding my very own. Now I had cried every day for six weeks! Not because I did not want to be a mother, not because I wasn't elated at being a mother, but because in the children's hospital we did at least get one weekend off every third weekend. Over the past six weeks there had been no nights off duty at all. Despite having a dedicated, hands-on husband, I was completely exhausted! My MOH wrote thanking me for my 'fine contribution'.

The social standing of doctors and nurses was then still clearly demarcated and I was asked how I could confess this weakness in front of so many nurses. Well, I replied, because it is true. In my ignorance I had thought that post-natal depression occurred in women who had not realised what an all-embracing matter motherhood was. I had never given due understanding to the impact of fatigue and hormone change. Even today, greater understanding and support is needed to help new mothers. Only 11% of maternity units in England currently hold the UNICEF Baby Friendly accreditation – a worldwide initiative to support breast feeding. When, in the late '60s, I first travelled to India and saw that every other being was a child and every young girl carried a baby on her hip, it struck me how artificial and segregated our society had become. Until modern times pregnant women usually had the support of their own mothers or other women family members, or at least of neighbouring women. To return from hospital to the fully carpeted, centrally heated home with running hot water may represent a previously undreamed of comfort, but today for many women, the first baby they hold in their arms is their own. It made me wonder whether parenting was instinctive or learned.

I cannot leave the images of children's hospitals of the '60s without describing Gloria. Today hospital administrators get concerned about 'blocked beds' – hospital beds with long-term occupants who do not actually need hospital care. Gloria was a young girl with cerebral palsy. She was black. She lay in her bed and smiled and grimaced at the nurses, for she could not speak. I cannot recall her being up and out of bed. At every ward round our consultant would play with Gloria's feet, which seemed to be constantly sheathed in purple woolly socks, and as she did so, our consultant would demand, 'And how is our little Gloria today?' Sister, clutching her ward book, would make some comment. Our consultant would smile at Gloria and our entourage would pass on to the next bed. Certainly our attitude to the physically and mentally handicapped children exemplified the worst of institutional thinking. The changes here are among the greatest I have observed. Whatever the problem, partnership with parents requires a different perspective from the attitudes of the '60s, and an approach where no child is ever written off.

Chapter Eight

Working in Multicultural London in the '60s

My Grandma, of the warmly loving hands, fell in love with my Grandpa when she heard him singing in the synagogue choir. Some half a century later, I fell in love with my young man, who was to become my husband, when I heard him sing with his north London school choir. His father was an Indian civil servant and the family had spent three years in London during the father's term of service at the High Commission. My young man, being the eldest of four, had been left behind to 'benefit' from a London university education. Like myself, his area of study had been chosen by his parents in consultation with his head-teacher. Whilst I pressed on with my undergraduate days, he studied down the road, at the London School of Economics. Having started his working life in a commercial bank, as soon as we could find an appropriate opening he escaped from the financial world and moved to administration in social welfare. When I was appointed to the Maternity and Child Health Clinic in Camden Town, he started work with the local voluntary body, Camden Council for Social Services. We read the same reports, and watched the workings of the same committees, councillors and lead officers but from differing perspectives. We compared notes about the families we worked with and wondered who had the more impossible task. Then, in 1966, the first Community Relations Officers were appointed and the post in Hackney was

43

to become his undertaking for the rest of the time that we lived in London.

For many people today, ticking boxes on an ethnic monitoring questionnaire form can be quite a challenge, but in the '60s it was a good deal simpler for the new immigrants who found themselves in Britain. Our clinic's main ethnic minority group were the Greek Cypriots. With the ending of colonialism, the demand for enosis (union with Greece) and the political changes being championed by Archbishop Makarios, Cyprus had emerged as a troubled island. Many Cypriots sought a more secure and economically promising life in Britain. Camden Town and Kentish Town already had Greek Orthodox churches with their Greek language and religious evening classes for children. Baklava and souvlakia were readily available in cafés and local stores and, when I joined the clinic, a Greek nurse was already on the staff. She came from mainland Greece, was married to an Englishman and had her own view regarding the new immigrants. Without her help as interpreter and her insight into cultural differences, how could I have coped? We worked together in the ante-natal and baby clinics, visiting the local schools together and running the evening family-planning clinic where we were introducing a culture that was new to these mothers. The Cypriot community, however, was not the only immigrant group using our clinic. We had a strong Irish community who had their own local social and cultural centre, first-generation West Indians whose children had joined them latterly, and recently arrived Bengali and Gujarati families. When the British Army pulled out of Aden, Chinese cooks who had withdrawn together with the military began to arrive with their families.

The 'push–pull' of migration is not new of course, but has been a constant theme throughout history. People have moved in search of new lands, new markets, expansionist settlements, while whole communities have been forcibly moved through political imperative, slavery and indentured labour. When my destitute eighteen-year-old great-grandfather arrived on the shores of Britain from Lithuania, he made his way to Leeds and to the synagogue. Being a presentable young man, he was soon married off to the Rabbi's daughter and the couple set out to seek a living in Edinburgh. Their first born was my grandfather, from whom I learned stories of the terrible poverty in their overcrowded tenement home. Grandpa shared the one bed with his seven brothers and sisters, 'counting bedbugs instead of sheep when we couldn't sleep'. Grandpa told of the anti-semitism they faced. He also told how moved he was when, as a child, he had witnessed the kindly welcome given by Christian ministers at the quayside to newly arriving, hungry, frightened Jewish refugees from the Russian pogroms. He was deeply moved when he saw a Christian minister remove his long coat and place it over the shoulders of a shivering Jewish woman.

My great-grandmother was a thinking woman – she would secretly go to hear Keir Hardie speak. She told her brood that they were never to be *wage-slaves* – with her German accent, this came out as *vayge slayfes*. Dr Jacobs was then busily pioneering the contraceptive pessary in Holland, but my great-grandmother had no choice and, like her contemporaries, had a brood of children. It was her two youngest daughters who had sought a better life in Australia. Hence, as a child, I really had thought that it was my cousins who had sent the sweets to my infant school.

When I was growing up in London, bombed sites were common, half-fallen houses were still evident and purple willow-herb and yellow wort flowers brightened the remaining rubble. It was not just London, but across Europe many towns were in ruins, millions of people were displaced and millions more had been lost in combat, air bombardment and extermination camps. Britain was not alone in experiencing a labour shortage. France, Holland and Germany also had pressing needs and their new workers were drawn from north Africa, the Dutch West Indies, Indonesia and Turkey. Holland led in setting up language classes, offering grants and engaging the support of voluntary organisations to encourage assimilation. Britain lagged behind. In the mid-60s our families lived in poorly adapted, multiple-occupied, degenerating Victorian terraced homes and were left to endure the vagaries of market forces. Even finding such accommodation was a problem. Throughout our area, the newsagents' rental advertisements read *No Irish, No Coloureds, No Dogs*. As a student, I too had lived in poor accommodation and knew what it was to share washing and cooking facilities and to live without access to a bathroom. For a student this is one thing – to raise families like that is quite another. We clinic staff saw how the advent of the pill brought relief to mothers who lacked bathroom privacy to insert and remove the Dutch cap. We noticed that when we were able to prescribe the pill, a whole new clientele arrived at our clinic.

The ill-effects of inadequate housing were evidently a major problem for our families. I started to write letters requesting 'health points' to help suffering families achieve better homes. After a few months I was summoned by our medical officer in charge of housing and health. I entered his office and sat facing him across his large desk. 'Look at this...' he cried, indicating row upon row of shelving towering behind him. 'These box files contain letter after letter requesting housing reviews, written by councillors, voluntary agencies and even our MP. If my own staff start writing letters, what am I going to do?'

At this time, without health points, it took twenty years to reach the top of the list. 'I will give you guidance,' he continued. 'If a child is run over on a zebra crossing and becomes paralysed from the waist downwards, and her mother lives on the third floor or above, then you may write me a letter. Anything less than that, please desist.'

By contrast, when I moved to Sussex eight years later, my request for health points saw families re-housed within months.

Our clinic building itself was hardly a child-friendly place. In the basement of a block of flats, just a few minutes' walk from Camden Town underground station, the windows were protected from vandalism by metal grilles. We had to use our fluorescent lighting all year round. Having parked their prams at street level, parents had to descend the steps carrying their babies and shepherding young children as best as they could. Access was not an issue then. Despite this, our superintendent (the lead health visitor) was justly proud of the clinic. She and her team made it bright with posters, comics and toys, and leaflets galore, and every mum had a warm welcome. Busy clinics, with sixty or so mothers, were a lively and noisy affair. Our health visitors certainly knew their families. At Christmas, decorated carrier bags filled with goodies were delivered to the most needy families, a practice which continues even today.

The needy children did suffer. Most of our immigrant mothers had to work to augment low family earnings. Many of the Cypriot women did machine stitching of garments at home. Their children were in playpens, passively sucking at bottles when what they needed was the language and play stimulation of nursery places. Our West Indian mums felt that they already spoke English, believed themselves to be Christians and had arrived in the heart of the 'mother country'. They encountered racial prejudice, lowly ill-paid work, rejection by overt colour bar from tenancies, and church rituals which differed from familiar practices. Many of these working mothers were also single parents – a residual by-product of family segregation under slavery. Without the extended family and before regulations were introduced, mothers were obliged to use sub-standard child-minding services where the children risked neglect. This worried us. We were also concerned about the small size and slow growth rate of the Asian babies. I still have a copy of a '60s health education leaflet written in Bengali advocating the dietary value of sliced white bread, raspberry jam and cornflakes – at a time when every corner shop in our area already sold rice, chapati flour, aubergines, peppers and garlic and a range of spices! These delights had yet to find their way through to the host country's dining table. Yes, we had much to learn.

Would our NHS have survived the '60s without our immigrant health workers? One third of our middle-grade doctors were from the Indian subcontinent, and we juniors were supervised by them. Oxfam produced a pamphlet entitled 'The Doctor-Go-Round', contrasting the number of British doctors leaving for North America and Australia with the number of Asian doctors arriving for post-graduate experience in the UK. Many of the Indian doctors passed their post-graduate exams and went home, others stayed to face the colour bar here. Yet others, with their Membership of a Royal College, moved to work in the private sector in the USA. In the '60s, it was only in the unpopular specialities of psychiatry and geriatrics that Indian doctors could achieve consultant posts in Britain. I remember the brave stance taken in the mid-70s by an Indian doctor who, having gained his Membership of the Royal College of Physicians, refused to take a geriatric consultant post. He was eventually awarded the first consultant post as a general physician to be held by an Indian.

The common response to Commonwealth immigration had undoubtedly been the entrenchment of the colour bar, with the branding of new immigrants as 'the colour problem'. Dr David Pitt, a GP from the West Indies, had his surgery down the road from our teaching hospital. He stood as prospective MP for Hampstead and later became Chairman of the Greater London Council. Elevated to Life Peer, he sat in the House of Lords. I well remember his address to our medical student debating society, where I was the statutory female on the committee. He asked why was it that coloured people were always represented in plays and films as 'the colour problem'. Why couldn't a black person just be a doctor, bus driver, mother or whatever the production required, without colour being the issue? It was not until the 1980s that representation noticeably changed, exemplified today through the range of characters of differing ethnic origin appearing in the soap operas. A similar revolution has taken place in athletics and sport. Norman Tebbitt, who served in Mrs Thatcher's cabinet, spoke of applying the 'Cricket Test'. He asked which side would Asians and West Indians, living in Britain, cheer at test matches. He got the answer less than one generation later when the English team was captained by Nasser Hussein and black athletes won gold medals for Britain! Whilst contemporary surveys show that covert racism continues within the NHS, ethnic minority doctors now lead all variety of specialities, sit on national committees and hold high office in medical organisations.

The merry-go-round of health carers continues. We remain short of NHS workers: a third of our doctors and nearly half our nurses are from overseas, mainly from the Philippines. The NHS runs an International Fellowship Scheme, recruiting specialist overseas doctors to consultant posts for a two-year experience in the UK. Whilst the scheme has a declared ethical dimension, with donor countries agreeing cooperation, overseas doctors have challenged this and dubbed the programme 'the great brain robbery'. Exchange of health personnel is an established tradition. British health staff serve in mission hospitals, overseas health projects and as volunteers. One of my fellow medical students had a three-month posting to the University of Ibadan, Nigeria. My medical student nephew worked in Malawi. A health visitor friend is recently returned from two years of mother and child health work with nomadic people in the foothills of the Himalayas. However, we need a fair system of exchange.

Given the popularity of ayurvedic medicine, homeopathy, acupuncture and tai chi, cultural profusion and pluralism are now as commonplace in health care as in many other aspects our daily lives. Such cultural assimilation exists alongside racism and discriminatory practices. Reflecting back to Dr Pitt's challenging question from the '60s, we may well ask how far are those of ethnic minority background fully incorporated within the image of the nation, and indeed, within the concept of the citizen of Europe?

Chapter Nine

Our Life in Multicultural London

In those early years of our marriage, we were living and working in Camden and felt well integrated into the local scene. I wore fairly formal clothes to work and scraped my hair up into a bun, held in place with numerous hairpins. On Saturday mornings, when I met our clinic mums at the local open-air market, I would be wearing jeans with my hair bouncing about in its ponytail. We loved the Greek Cypriot shops with their good olive oil, Mediterranean vegetables and syrup-filled sweets. What joy to have lived opposite the Cypriot bakery, buying hot bread at unsocial hours. With the advent of Indian grocery stores selling spices and lentils, my husband could cook his familiar dishes to his heart's content ... and ours. When our first child started her school, she was one among many others from all sorts of backgrounds. I took this cultural mix for granted and did not realise till I moved to Sussex how special it had been. It was unseen by my eyes because I had been accustomed to living in a mixed community.

My parents had referred to Golders Green as a 'cosmopolitan area'. As a child I had commonly heard English spoken with German, Hungarian and Polish accents. My mother's women friends had exotic and attractive names. They would expressively hug and kiss us children. My paternal grandparents always spoke in Yiddish to my father and, apart from their urging us to eat at those Sunday teas, I cannot recall chats with them that mirrored the stories I heard from Grandpa at home. We ate delicacies from across Europe. Our local political demonstrations were held at 'Appendrodt's Corner'. This was a public paved area outside the Austrian-style coffee and pastry shop, which we occasionally visited for strudel and other treats. Even in the '50s our vista was wider than just the continental exiles from fascism. Dad, with his international interests, hosted doctors from eastern Europe and the Commonwealth. Some stayed in our home. One doctor from the Gold Coast (now Ghana) named his daughter after me, as did an Italian from north Italy. A charming south Indian doctor, Dr Nair, often stayed at our home and took us out for my first ever Indian meal when I was thirteen. There were just some half dozen Indian restaurants in London then, not the thousands of today.

Grandpa too provoked our wider appreciation. When Grandpa retired from his cleaning and dyeing business, he was so bored that he began a new import business, which he ran from his bedroom in our home. As the business grew, his papers and typewriter migrated to the kitchen. We had to clear the 'office' table before meals. Returning from a family holiday, we discovered a shed had sprouted in the garden. The office had moved out there. The garden eventually shrank under a series of sheds! Grandpa was importing stainless steel scissors and manicure sets from Solingen. He had approached that town because he liked the sound of the name; it seemed to him like a bell. He next learned that Pakistan could undercut Germany and so started trading with Sialkot City. One Pakistani businessman came to our home accompanied by his wife, who carried a zari-embroidered handbag. Ever the magpie, Grandpa was fascinated by this silver embroidery. My brother had just won his prized scholarship to a well regarded boys' grammar school. Grandpa asked whether a zari-embroidered blazer badge could be made. That was how his last business started – and how all my girl friends received zari-embroidered evening bags with matching belts. Well, wasp-waists were the great fashion.

Through Grandpa, I received my first picture book of Indian dance – complete with a tinkling bell, a silver-encrusted sari, and, with my brother and the son of one of Grandpa's business associates, went to a sitar concert in the days when no other non-Indian would be in the audience. It was at Friends' Meeting House in Euston. I recall wondering why the audience was calling out 'wah, wah' at key moments, and why there was so much audience head movement, and I clearly remember sitting looking at the clock, wondering how time could pass so slowly! Several years later, I learned to listen to the music through the films of Satyajit Ray. More than a decade later Grandpa's business provided my entry to the Muslim household in Varanasi which had become his main supplier. Badges and bags kept Grandpa busy till his final departure. For all his early deprivation, he was still actively working till the day he died, at ninety. Thus it was that, by the time I reached medical school, I was so used to meeting people from all parts of the world that I was astonished when my colleague was startled to find that she had three Jewish girls in her class.

The way we see others is always conditioned by our own experiences. When my husband and I were looking for digs after I had qualified, we enquired at a Greek Cypriot lettings agency. We were passed a card describing the rental. My husband faltered: 'Excuse me, it clearly says "no coloured".'

Our agent surveyed my husband from head to toe. 'Oh no, sir,' he confidently replied, 'I would not call you coloured.'

We found our digs from a notice in a shop window, reading 'Unconventional, but not students'. We were both graduates and a married couple, but I was living in the hospital and could only come home on those odd weekends off duty. There were no married quarters in the hospitals – when my husband did illicitly stay in the hospital on the odd night, we would squeeze together in a single bed and I would have to smuggle him out in the morning. Our digs comprised a bedroom, a lovely front room with four long Georgian windows, and, down a couple of steps, a tiny kitchen with a sink. The toilet was communal, there was no bathroom available for our use. I used to bathe at the hospital and my husband used to drop in on a neighbouring friend! We stayed there for four years and were very happy. We had a well-known comedian living below us and a fine cellist upstairs who gave us concert tickets. We had no student loans to pay off, but making our way in those early years was not easy.

On completing my hospital work and starting at the clinic in Camden Town, we applied for a mortgage on a lovely house within walking distance of the clinic. Our solicitor, a close friend, advised against this purchase as he considered that the area could become a slum clearance area and we could become victims of a compulsory purchase order. I knew how desperate the housing need was in the borough and could not see how such lovely Victorian houses might be demolished. They just needed renovation and repair! We lived for eight years in that solid Victorian house, doing much of the decoration and improvement ourselves. We could not have raised a mortgage on just our own incomes, so we declared that we would be renting out the first floor to tenants. Two younger friends of ours, who worked in community theatre, lodged with us for the duration of our stay. My husband was working in Hackney and I was working in Camden Town. On Monday mornings we would say goodbye ... see you on Friday night! He had regular evening meetings where most of his community connections were made, I had my evening family-planning clinic. Eventually, both our children were born during our time at that house.

In those first years of our marriage we could not afford to travel to India to meet the family, as our two fares would have cost my entire annual income. Instead we used to go for camping holidays in our Mini with a tent that was just a piece of white cloth on two poles, held down with camping pegs. We travelled around Britain, from Cornwall to Yorkshire and the Lake District. We bravely drove down the Rhine and across Bavaria to stay with very close friends in north Italy. In 1967, Poland was opened to independent visits for foreign travellers instead of just accompanied tours. We madly decided to go! It was a nightmare. Campsites were designated fields without any facilities at all. When we drove into town in the early morning we were always too late to find food to buy in the shops. Luckily, the Polish campers we met at the sites were fascinated by us. They shared their camp-fire stews with us, invited us to travel with them and showed us aspects of the country we would otherwise never have seen. We were particularly befriended by a young scientist called Marek who had qualified at the university in Leningrad. We spent a great week with him, finally staying at his parents' flat in Warsaw. When we said our goodbyes, he told us he was longing to join a course he had read about at Cambridge University but that he needed sponsorship from someone in Britain. We wrote to the authorities every year for the next four years offering this, until he was finally able to stay with us.

During the period that Marek lodged with us downstairs, our community theatre friends upstairs were giving shelter to a Vietnam draft dodger called Adrian. His greatest desire was to go to Moscow to join the famous Clown Circus School. Thus it was that in our home, Marek with his eyes turned firmly to the West, translated into Russian the letter from American Adrian whose eyes were definitely focused on the East. We certainly lived in a mixed-up world.

Chapter Ten

The Swinging Sixties: A Great Time to Work

We had grown up in the 1950s, the era of 'you never had it so good'. We had witnessed the success of the Mini, the first motorway, the introduction of hire purchase credit facility and home television sets. Grandpa, after the horror and acute sense of shame at his initial poverty, lived to experience the comforts of the affluent society. Professor Galbraith, however, had pointed up the co-existence of public squalor. From the USA came the notion of the 'rat race'. As students we learned about the diseases of affluence – the heart attacks and strokes haunting high-powered businessmen with their working lunches and hectic lives. That association was later unhooked when it was shown that men in semi-skilled and unskilled jobs succumbed equally to heart disease. Among the losers in the rat race were the middle-class women, house-bound in their superb homes, suffering suburban neurosis induced by a life spent polishing tables and adjusting ornaments in their ideal home. But the real issues of health and social class were gaining a higher profile.

Our concerns about our Camden Town families were not passing unnoticed by the authorities. The 1964 Wilson government began to steer change, and this felt to be an exciting time of hopeful developments. There was a flurry of reports about housing. In 1966 the TV documentary-style drama *Cathy Come Home* thoroughly shocked viewers. It traced the plight of a homeless young couple and their children experiencing the enforced break-up of the family because of their inability to find accommodation. Viewers were disturbed by the unabashed officiousness of the welfare officers. Each year 4000 children were being received into care because of homelessness. It was estimated that one million unfit houses continued to be occupied. The voluntary organisation Shelter was set up. GPs were given additional allowances for working in deprived areas. Supplementary Benefits replaced the National Assistance 'dole money'.

What about education? Secondary school selection, with Edward's dreaded eleven-plus scholarship papers, was abolished in 1965. With selection replaced by entry at eleven-plus to comprehensive education, the competitive elements in primary schooling could be relaxed. Educationalists began to talk about the yardstick of attainment being the child's personal potential. What mattered was not who was top of the class, but how far each child could be enabled to develop his/her full abilities. Creativity, musicality, athleticism and other attributes and achievements could be valued alongside the ability to be quick at maths, competent at spelling or good at 'intelligence tests'. For us in community health, the pivotal moment was the publication of the Plowden Report in 1967, recommending a programme to meet the needs of pre-school and primary schoolchildren in deprived areas. We in Camden Town suddenly found ourselves working in an 'Educational Priority Area' (EPA).

There had already been a major slum clearance of the decaying Victorian mansions behind Camden High Street, with an extensive development of low-rise, high-density maisonette housing. Shops, newsagents and a community hall were also built. During the school summer holiday following the confirmation of our EPA status, prefab nursery classes sprouted in each playground of our old Victorian primary schools. Child health staff were asked to identify the under fives with language and developmental needs who would benefit from a nursery place. Of course we had no problem finding such children! Alongside such developments, pre-school playgroups and after-school clubs were springing up and receiving new money – my husband was able to support applications in Hackney. Support for children was on track.

Part of my work then was to visit some half dozen primary schools and medically examine the new entrants and all eight-year-olds. This was a terribly public affair. Across a long table sat the head-teacher and the education welfare officer both busily taking notes. The school nurse would do her initial assessment of growth and vision and then escort the child and mother into this gathering. I would start with an open-ended enquiry to the mother about how she felt her child was settling into school. Amongst the twelve children I would see in a morning, there was always at least one mother who, in response to my first question, would break down and cry. I felt terrible. This was totally the wrong environment in which to take up these concerns, there was never the time to listen properly and it seemed so wrong to ask questions if you were not prepared for worrying answers. I requested an appointment to see our Medical Officer of Health.

Luckily, Dr Harding was a man of energy and vision. I had already met him during my year on the Public Health post-graduate course. He had wryly told us then that medical care was only one small part of social care provided in the community. At our meeting now, he told me that the council was commissioning a three-year survey of the needs of families, to be conducted by a team of medical sociologists. The maternity hospitals were going to share ante-natal care with district midwives. We clinic doctors would no longer be required for that work, releasing us to focus on family work. Our maternity and child welfare clinics were to be developed into family welfare clinics. Thus it was that I started my first 'Family Clinics'. I was supported by a medical social worker who, although long resident in London, had been born in India. We started with two clinics, each at either end of my patch. When I met distressed mothers at the schools, I could thankfully offer an appointment in the privacy of the clinic. We were kept very busy. My social worker colleague knew how to tap sources of practical help. We were even able to recommend families for a week's convalescent holiday at the seaside. Looking back, I can readily illustrate the contrast between the London and the Sussex mothers, for I well remember that I had been visiting the Sussex schools for more than two years before any mother broke down and cried at a routine health session.

The Camden primary head-teachers had a high level of commitment to the children. In one school we were really struggling with the children's disturbed and antisocial behaviour. After parking meters were extended to Camden Town, our head-teacher used to remove the shoes from certain of our lads during the lunch break to prevent them from going out to rob the meters. He and I sat down together to make a list of the children who worried us the most. We drew up profiles of the children to see how we could help. Unsurprisingly, the majority were boys between the ages of eight and ten, mostly without an effective father-figure. Either the father had deserted – far more common than divorce at that time – or was known to suffer from mental illness, or was undermined by unemployment. We applied for, and achieved, a male teacher for an 'opportunity class' to be held in our school for these boys. It seems surprising now that such proposals found funding through the EPA schemes.

Around this time, I was sent on a training course in the measurement of intelligence, run by educational psychologists. Although I never used this training to officially assess children, what I learned proved invaluable to my understanding of children. We used the Stanford Binet Intelligence Test – the same test my father had used when preparing me for the eleven-plus scholarship. It was an interesting test and could be great fun too, but had a heavy language bias. At that time, measurement of a child's intelligence carried a certain confidence, both about present ability and future prediction. Children who scored a quotient below 70 (100 representing average intelligence) were selected out for Educationally Subnormal schools (ESNs). It was believed that children would respond better in small classes with a reduced curriculum, presented at an easier level.

In the mid-60s there was a scandal about the over-representation of Afro-Caribbean children in the ESN schools of Inner London. Our tutors addressed this issue. One type of question in the Stanford Binet test was to draw out similarities and differences. One tutor told of a West Indian boy who was asked in what way wine and beer were similar and in what way different. The boy looked puzzled. The examiner, being allowed one set prompt question, then asked: What is wine? The boy replied: A drink with alcohol that makes you feel good. He was then asked: What is beer? The boy responded: A brown furry animal that walks on four legs.

This anecdote was very much in my mind when I was let loose in an ESN school and presented with a West Indian boy on whom to practise assessment. I smiled at the boy. He smiled back. I carefully went through the test, asking the prompt questions that were allowed. Checking my results at the end, I found he had scored 100, an average score. My tutor was quite taken aback and promised a formal re-assessment. But that experience taught me much. The Stanford Binet Test was abandoned in the 1970s and scales were introduced that assessed both language-based intelligence and non-verbal reasoning. It was not just our method of testing which changed; rather it was our concepts of the certainty of future prediction, of the value of segregated education and our understanding of cultural factors, including social class experience, that confounded testing.

This brings me to the work of the National Children's Bureau (NCB) which was to become a source of sustenance for my own work over the next thirty years. A long-standing friend of ours became the statistician at the NCB. He invited me over to the neighbouring borough of Islington to visit the Bureau and learn about their work on the National Child Development Study. This programme had captured nearly 16,000 children born in one week in March 1958. The children and their families were being monitored; looking at birth history, health, development, educational attainment, home and environment – the issues that were intriguing me. A preliminary report had been published in 1966. Our friend was working on the data for the second report looking at outcomes for the children at age seven years. This work transcended our anecdotal experiences, providing a sweeping overview of British children. Published in 1972, *From Birth to Seven* was aimed at teachers, doctors, social workers and others who worked with children. It described British children as of two nations: those of the leafy suburbs where families lived with access to well-paid jobs, new schools, shops and parks, and the many others who lived in overcrowded accommodation, where families suffered unemployment and old schools with overworked staff and lacked access to open space.

The whole report was fascinating. The variation between the affluent suburb and inner-city was shocking, reflecting the difference between Edward and myself. The diagram from the book which I used thereafter in my teaching, was the cycle of failure interlinking emotional difficulties with poor school performance. How could Edward, in his red and grey uniform, with no concerned parents to support him, have kept pace in the competitive race for those contested scholarship places? We had already had Sir Keith Joseph's controversial *Cycle of Deprivation*. The Bureau's publication presented the dynamics of what happens to disadvantaged children inside our schools.

It is not coal, nor fertile fields, nor fishing grounds, that are the main natural resource of a country. It is the children. The reports of this period were acknowledging this in their titles: *Half our Future, All Our Future, Fit for the Future*. The focus of my interest turned to the children. I needed to know more about health and education, how schools worked, how schools could support individual children. I raided the education shelves of Dillons University Bookshop. I found the wonderful reports of John and Elizabeth Newson describing four-year-olds in Nottingham and picturing the lives of seven-year-olds in their homes. I found

John Holt's books on how children fail and how they escape from childhood. I devoured the Penguin Education Specials then in publication, especially Sir Alec Clegg's writing on children in distress, and a shocking book from America, Jonathan Kozol's account of the fate of black children in Boston schools entitled *Death at an Early Age.* Thus it was, that when I cut down to part-time work after our first child was born, I asked that my programme should concentrate on work in the School Health Service.

Chapter Eleven

Return to Academia

My Dad saw my brother graduate, but sadly he never lived to see me qualify. He died tragically and unexpectedly, in his early fifties, the Christmas after the Cuban missile crisis. I had just three months to go before my final exams. It was a terrible winter, we were all stunned. Granny had clung to me weeping: 'My rock, my rock of Gibraltar is gone.' It was a terrible time for us all. I knew I had to pass my exams first go. I went over all the papers of the preceding seven years practising model answers, in between succumbing to bouts of sudden weeping. My medical friends knew what I was going through and felt very sorry for me when I walked out early from each final paper. I had been so hyped up and ready to write that I worked frenetically through the questions, all of which I had met in some form or other on the past papers I had worked at. Against the odds, I did manage to qualify that spring.

My grandparents saw all three grandchildren graduate: two doctors and a mathematician. It was Granny's dearest wish that I should be a paediatrician and I was certainly attracted to working with children – perhaps it was the influence of those early puppet shows at the day nurseries. I was passed over at my first interview and took a temporary paediatric job. That morning, when I succeeded in being offered my first proper paediatric post, I phoned my Mum in the lunch hour to let her know. Granny died that afternoon. She had been ill and having treatment for nine months; we never heard her complain. She was still cooking Sunday lunch the day before she died. My girl friends, who knew Granny from our school days, also cried for her.

After gaining my post-graduate Diploma in Child Health, I was at another professional crossroads. I was exhausted by the residential work. I had worried much about the children we had treated with recurrent illnesses and the impact of their living conditions. I suppose all that early experience with my Dad must have conditioned my thinking. I chose to enrol in the one-year academic course in Public Health. The Dean, remembering my father, warmly accepted me on the course. What a relief it was to be a student again, when evenings and weekends were once more our own. I made many new friends that year among the other doctors on the course. Some from overseas were regular visitors to our digs, grateful to escape from hostel living and for the amazing meals my husband would cook for them in our tiny kitchen.

We met a fine Sudanese doctor from the Arabic north, who later wrote about the enormous load of responsibility he carried on his return to work in the southern part of that country. We had given him a copy of my parents' book *From Witchcraft to World Health*. He wrote saying that his southern health station was just the place to read it.

'The people here are very poor, they go naked or half naked at best. All of them suffer from one or more diseases which your father called the diseases of ignorance and poverty'.

He was not only running the clinic caring for the local population and his own staff, but he was also the director of the 500-bed hospital. He ended by writing, 'I think I have too much work for one man.' Another friend was from Rhodesia, but of Welsh extraction. He was running what he called Our Crusade to eradicate tuberculosis. He railed against the lack of any serious attempt to consistently apply what is already known. We also befriended two English doctors who had been working overseas, one in mission hospitals in Sikkhim, the other in the Solomon

Islands – he gave us a shark's tooth spear! We were fascinated by all their experiences and stories.

Following our written exams at the end of the academic year, we had to present before a panel of the professors and academics. I nervously looked up awaiting my first question. I was stunned when it was, 'Are you married?'

I replied that I was. The Professor looked disappointed. He paused, then brightening up, asked, 'Do you practise in your maiden name?'

I replied that I did. Most of my married women friends had taken their husband's name, but I had not.

'Aha!' he exclaimed, naming my Dad. 'Then are you a relation?'

'He was my father,' I replied.

'That then explains your written papers. I have nothing else to ask.' Thus ended my oral examination ... a far cry from my Membership oral which I attended a decade later!

In the mid-60s, Public Health was definitely a Cinderella speciality with poor standing among the rest of the medical fraternity. Public Health, it was sneered, was the soft option for the boys and pin money for the girls. It was one of the few specialities that offered women part-time work. Dr Harding, my Camden boss, was actively pioneering change, working for an academic base for Public Health within the Royal College of Physicians. This was achieved in the '70s. Thus, by the time the Thatcher government brought in the NHS reforms, it was the strengthened Public Health Departments that were to commission services, set targets and monitor the audit of clinical work.

Early in the '70s a major commission was set up to overview the health needs and health services for children, chaired by Professor Donald Court. We waited long and eagerly for the report and welcomed *Fit for the Future* with great satisfaction when it appeared in 1976. It described what we knew. The report talked about the rearing of the young as the fundamental issue in human society. Yes, oh yes! Whilst living conditions had greatly improved since the war, the majority of children had exchanged stability for prosperity and the minority were as disadvantaged as ever, the shadows of disadvantage casting long shadows forward. Yes, again yes, for Edward and all the others! It should be the objective of a civilised society to ameliorate the effects of disadvantage. We needed to work towards far greater partnership with parents, especially for the million children being raised in single parent families. Yes, oh yes – this was the first time I had read about 'partnership'. The link between health and education was raised as one of the most important aspects of paediatrics. A new post was recommended: that of consultant community paediatrician, with the duty to bear oversight of the conditions of the children and with responsibility to develop ways of supporting the disadvantaged, of protecting their health and their progress. Yes, that was the work I wanted to do! Above all, warned the report, a change in attitude was needed, a greater care for the child and the family, and better information and support for parents, to be provided in a more acceptable manner.

Dad had taught me always to begin at the top and work downwards. I went to a meeting of the Socialist Medical Association at the Houses of Parliament where Professor Court was commenting on the report. I approached him at the end, talked about my work and asked him about the new consultant posts.

'You are just the sort of doctor we had in mind,' he replied encouragingly, 'but you must qualify as a member of one of the Royal Colleges.'

I was living in Sussex with our two young children then, our son was still at playgroup. What could I do? I wrote to Dr Harding for advice. He introduced me to one of the professors at the University of Sussex who became my mentor over the next few years. I did not realise, at first, that he was also the husband of one of my colleagues in our Sussex child health team. I remember going to the university and pouring out all my angry frustrations about the inadequacies of our work system. He helped me enormously, encouraging me to do a survey on the needs of the children I saw at my Lewes Family Clinic and asking how far I was meeting the real needs in the community. We had a clinic group and a control group and the cross-referencing was fascinating. I worked away at this while my own kids had their friends round to play after school. It made it easier to write when they were occupied with their own pals. My work was submitted to the ivory towers in London and I waited.

The examiners called me up to tell me that my work had been referred and I would have to revise large sections. I was horribly concerned and nervously went to meet them. In the discussion, I was repeatedly advised to 'beef up the epidemiology'. (It began to sound like the catch phrase from a song!) The descriptive writing about the children's problems was fine. The academic analysis was full of loopholes. My conclusions were all about how the service should be developed to meet the needs I had described. I was frankly told that they understood what I was writing about, but this was not appropriate for an academic dissertation. I should address the strengths and weaknesses of the study not the issues more appropriately addressed in a policy paper.

'If we were to accept your paper and put it on the shelf, then one day a fellow academic might read it and question why it had been accepted.'

'I didn't write this paper to gather dust on the shelf,' I exclaimed. 'I wrote it to change the service!'

I was talked out. The woman examiner quietly approached me after the interview saying consolingly, 'If you are prepared to prostitute your work, you can give us what we need with a couple of weeks' rewriting.'

I seethed all the way home on the train, vowing not to change a word. Of course, I cooled down, went back to see my professor, and did what was required, but added my service plan as an appendix. I was awarded my Membership and spent the next many years training others and participating in service development plans along the lines I had written about, but I did not get my consultant community paediatrician grade for a further twenty years. That, however, is another story.

Chapter Twelve

The Struggle for Health Education in Schools

I had been in my early twenties when it had been my task to safely complete over a hundred abortions, and not much older when I met the unmarried mothers from the Mother and Baby Homes. I was troubled by the extent of the continuing ignorance and vulnerability of young girls. In the 1880s Dr Annie McCall had firmly declared that it was the duty of educated women to come to the rescue of less favoured women; she urged her students to teach, constantly teach in a deeply friendly manner. In those Swinging Sixties, while the Beatles were singing *All you need is love*, who was teaching the young about sexuality?

I turned out to be the youngest of the sixty doctors on my Public Health course. Only a handful of us were women and half the students were from overseas. It proved to be a great year – particularly to enjoy the freedom of student life again after the privations of residential hospital posts. I met an old friend from my undergraduate days. He had been out in the Bahamas and was now studying tropical public health. I asked whether he was going to go back.

'No fear,' he replied. 'When I went out there I knew nothing about tropical medicine. Now I know about those diseases there's no way I'll go back!' He had always been good fun to know. I recalled that he had been sick after his first birth delivery. On giving up the tropics, he became an obstetrician!

Our class was divided into groups for project work – mine included my friends from Sudan and Rhodesia. We opted to do our project on health education in schools. With our tutor's support, we drew up a questionnaire to test the understanding of teenagers on various health topics including questions on sexual knowledge. We had access to pupils in four comprehensive schools, including single-sex and mixed-sex schools. A close friend of mine was then studying for her teacher training qualification and she negotiated entry into her college so we could explore the attitudes to health education of the trainee teachers. For all our enthusiasm, I cannot say we achieved any great breakthrough. It was tedious, an absolute bind, to collate the responses to the questionnaires and the only real result was the hardening of our determination to 'do something' about health education, wherever we came from.

When I joined the Camden team, I declared my interest in this area and was asked to spend one session each week with the borough's Health Education Officer. We would choose a monthly topic, hunt out good posters and leaflets, and write up our own 'fact sheet' pointing up issues we deemed to be of topical interest for our local public. We sent these collections to the local libraries, clinics, day nurseries and others who would display the material. But I really wanted to get into the schools. I had done some sessions in my primary schools on 'How Your Body Works' which the children had enjoyed. The ten-year-olds had crowded round to see and handle medical instruments, they had felt their own heart beat, and joined in when I showed how to test hearing and eye movements. I had received a delightful set of drawings from one class to thank me: Jody wanted me to come again 'because it was goog', Andrew liked the stethoscope, Lenny wrote to thank me for the bit about the brain. But how was I going to get entry into the secondary schools where the needs for health education were arguably even greater? An old friend came to the rescue.

When I was eleven years old, my parents had to name three secondary schools for me in order of preference. My primary-school head-teacher had warned against their first choice, explaining that no girl from his council school had ever gained admission to that grammar school. Applicants who passed the scholarship papers also had to attend a selective entrance interview. My parents must have shielded me, for I had no idea at the time of the importance of that spring-time interview. A girl in a green check dress with long blonde plaits sat next to me, nervously awaiting her turn. She reached out for my hand and held it in her own. I was the only entrant from my primary school to my new school that memorable September and there, in my new class, was the girl with the green dress – only now she was in brown (called *nigger brown* in those days), like the rest of us. We became friends, went through our school years as friends and are still friends today over half a century later. It was with her that I had cried during the dinner hour after my career interview. She went on to Cambridge University to read history. Gaining a Churchill Fellowship, she spent time in the United States and then came home the long way round, visiting Japan and India. Thus she met my in-laws and the grandparents in Delhi, years before I ever had that opportunity.

When I started work in Camden Town, this friend was already head of history at the local girls' grammar school – the sister-school to the one we had attended. I talked to her about my work and about what I really wanted to do. She spoke to her head-teacher and I received a generous offer. Not only was I invited to be the named school doctor (which was a feather in the cap for my MOH as we provided that role in council schools but not in the private or direct-grant sector), but I was also invited to participate in direct class teaching on health topics. I was assigned to meet the fourth years (fourteen-year-olds) and the sixth form (seventeen-year-olds). With the younger teenagers I did an off-the-cuff session, responding to issues they raised on an ad-hoc basis. In fact, for me that meant scanning the Sunday colour supplements each week to see which health issues had just been featured. With the older girls I prepared a formal course looking at our health needs from pregnancy and birth, through the various stages of life, to old age. I felt this to be the best approach and was gratified to find how well it was received. A 'parents' evening' was soon added, where I had to answer parents' questions on a whole range of subjects related to young people's health. At that time, I myself was only just in my thirties with two very young children. The 'thank-you' letters from the parent sessions were greatly encouraging – I remember that one spoke of the relief in knowing that there was 'a sane, humorous professional' available to the girls.

Whilst the impetus for this work came from witnessing the casualties of unprotected sex, it was the growing abuse of mind-affecting drugs which opened up entry into the secondary schools. As medical students, we had participated in a class tutorial on drugs affecting the brain. We had been divided into three groups and given either a stimulant, a depressant or a non-active agent. No one knew what they had taken. We performed skill tests before and after taking our pills. My partner had obviously been given a depressant; he became more and more morose as the afternoon progressed, which was quite out of character. I, by contrast, became highly elated. I found ways to cheat at the tests by double stabbing at the moving dots with my electronic probe so that my scores went way up. I was excitedly and noisily showing off. At the end of the period, the tutor told us what we had each taken. My partner had indeed been given a depressant, but I had been given a non-active pill. There is a moral in that story!

Of course people have always chewed, brewed and smoked various plants to exploit their effects on mood and emotional sensibility. Mind-affecting painkillers were derived from opium in the nineteenth century – morphia in 1803 and heroin in 1896 – and their addictive powers were known from the earliest days. Up to the mid-60s, most registered heroin addicts had actually been introduced to the drug as part of clinical treatment, and were termed 'therapeutic' addicts.

74

In 1964, for the first time, the number of addicted heroin users who had experimented for pleasure reached the same level as 'therapeutic' addicts. In the following two years the number of registered 'non-therapeutic' users soared from 300 to over 1000. Whilst this was still more than ten times lower than the rate of addiction in the USA and a thousand times lower than that in Hong Kong, there was a real sense of alarm. Over the same period, the numbers experimenting with the hallucinatory drug lysergic acid diethylamide (LSD) rose from a few hundred to over 2000. Cannabis was becoming increasingly popular among students, while the amphetamines, or purple hearts, which had been widely prescribed to lift the depression of suburban housewives, were gaining popularity with the young to enhance their partying. The drug culture found overt expression among the 'hippies' who 'turned on, tuned in and dropped out'. Some users suffered mental confusion. Those who were disturbed after using LSD were dubbed 'acid heads' and those affected by the over-use of cannabis, 'pot heads'. The favoured garb of tie-dyed loose clothing and sandals accompanied the eastward-facing embrace of Zen Buddhism, incense and Indian ragas. Head-teachers were concerned.

Our Health Department started to receive invitations to visit the secondary schools to give talks on the dangers of drugs. I well remember my first visit with our Health Education Officer to a local boys' comprehensive school. The whole school was assembled in the hall where we showed an educational film. Following this, I invited questions. The boys were totally silent and all the enquiries came from staff sitting around the edge of the hall. It was awful! I knew we should never present like that again. Any session about drugs must be one talk in a set of at least six, including other health topics and delivered in small groups. We never had the chance to run such a programme in the state schools but one of the small private schools picked this up. Before I could be let loose on the boys, I had to attend a parents' evening where I could be grilled and vetted by the parents so their boys could attend my set of six classes. I must have passed this initiation by fire, because I received appreciative letters and the headmaster invited me to repeat and increase the set of talks. This work was an optional extra on my part-time programme for Wednesday afternoons. The school was near Regent's Park and Mum would collect my two children and take them for a drive around the Outer Circle of the park to see the animals in the zoo while I did my hour with the boys.

Another friend of ours was working as Director with BBC Schools Television. He invited me to help as medical advisor on school TV programmes – I even appeared in some. My six-year-old nephew was very upset when he waved to me when he saw me on television in his school class and I did not wave back. I wrote a couple of books, one for primary-age children about germs, immunisation and keeping healthy, the other for teenagers based on my talks. Adult viewers also wanted information about sex and drugs. I was invited to appear on *Doctor on Call* and other television programmes.

Changing behaviour involves far more than the transmission of knowledge. During our Public Health course we had been shown a graph which illustrated how, in the ten years after Sir Richard Doll had demonstrated the link between cigarette smoking and lung cancer, doctors were increasingly giving up smoking and their lung cancer rates were already falling. However the public's smoking habits had continued to increase, as had their lung cancer rates. That knowledge by itself rarely changes attitude, is illustrated by the fact that hospital nurses continued with high smoking levels. It took over fifty years after the smoking study, before the government legislated about smoking in public places.

In the mid-60s, we were certainly horrified when the number of registered heroin addicts topped a thousand. Today, despite the numerous studies of the paths that lead to the tragedy of addiction and the many imaginative, valiant anti-drug programmes, we have now over 100,000 heroin addicts; drugs are big business, and drug crime is pervasive.

Our random efforts at health education continued. In Sussex, I was still doing occasional classes in mixed comprehensive schools and regular parents' evenings through the '70s and into the '80s. These evening invitations ended when schools had to pay to use their own premises after school hours. The schools eventually introduced classroom programmes with a planned curriculum of personal social education. School nurses trained up and became active educators. Many school nurses today also provide family-planning services and are therefore well placed to integrate their work in schools with their work in local family-planning clinics. Some staff mobile health-education vans which visit housing estates to meet enquiries from the young. Others work in dedicated premises known as Health Education Shops which provide information and advice. All this is such an advance on our ad-hoc efforts. Today, in the boys' school which had opted for my set of talks, the deputy head, who is also a qualified counsellor, delivers the Personal, Social, Health and Citizenship course. She happens to be the daughter of my history-teacher friend, the girl in the green dress who had got me my first invitation!

The last school programme in which I took part was, by chance, in my own daughter's school when she was fourteen years old. She and her friends heard me take part in the introductory session for the whole school year, but I had asked the organiser to ensure she was not in my small group. At the end of the day, a girl in my group clutched at my arm saying wistfully, 'I wish you was my mum.'

A UNICEF report on teenage pregnancy rates in 2002 showed that UK rates are the highest in Europe and more than three times the rates in France, Spain, Italy, Denmark and Sweden. Sexual imagery permeates many aspects of life in all these countries. So how are young people encouraged to cope successfully with their emergent sexuality in some countries, while in others they lack effective support? We need an evaluated school curriculum delivered by teachers, covering health and social care, good citizenship and participation, together with back-up from health staff, particularly school nurses. However, it is not just school education, nor even loving parental care that protects young people, although both have a major contribution to make. The culture of the group is also highly significant and it is in this area that there have been dramatic changes during my working life.

Looking back, was all that thought and effort spent on health education a waste of a doctor's time? I know I learned from every teaching and parent session, especially from those in socially mixed communities. Some twenty years after the Camden classes, following an address I gave to a public meeting in the Hastings area about the medical response to nuclear weapons, a woman from the audience approached me. She commented that she thought that I had been the doctor who had spoken on health topics at her school in her teenage years. On checking which had been her school, I affirmed this was so. She then paused and thoughtfully commented that those talks had affected her throughout her life – she had never forgotten them.

Chapter Thirteen

Working Mums

Shirley, Stella and I were good friends at medical school and, despite our widely different and geographically separated lives, we have remained in touch and continue to enjoy occasional reunions. In our student days, we were the 'unconventional girls'. We wore ultra-long earrings, marched to Aldermaston, demonstrated against apartheid. We knew each other's parents, we spent holidays together and we marked each other's progress through medical school. We all expected to get married and have children. We all did – marrying in our early twenties around the time we qualified as doctors. On starting our families we faced three choices. Shirley placed her daughter in the crèche and continued to work full-time. Stella married a doctor and gave up work for several years while her two children were young. I worked part-time, just four half-days when ours were small. I increased my hours when they were school-aged and returned to full-time when they were in their teens. Each of these choices about work and parenting had its own difficulties.

When our two children were under five, I needed help to do those four clinics a week. My Mum could do occasional back-up, but had other responsibilities and was already suffering from indifferent health. I advertised for an older woman to help. The first respondent was a traditional nanny, in starched uniform and equally starched manner. Then Mrs T came along. She lifted up our four-week-old daughter, who suddenly gave her first smile, thus choosing her own carer. Mrs T proved to be a gentle and caring but strong person. She could not have been kinder or more patient with the children or more supportive to us. In those early months I certainly needed support! Who on earth decided that statutory maternity leave should start twelve weeks before and end six weeks after the birth? No one who has ever had a baby would make such laws. When I restarted work, night waking to feed our baby was the norm, and the return to work felt awful. Although I was only working four half-days a week, I was utterly exhausted. Punished the first time round, I applied for a month's unpaid leave in addition to the statutory six weeks with our second baby, but even ten weeks felt too early to return to work. Thankfully fathers now have paternity leave, and mothers' jobs are protected for the first year.

I found that a strict mental discipline was essential when switching from doctoring to mothering. At the end of the morning clinic my head would be full of unfinished problems – letters to be sent off, results to be chased up, decisions for individual children yet to be made. I learned to consciously close down on work-thinking when I reached a particular crossroads close to our Victorian home. I would then turn my mind completely to our little ones and be ready to greet them as I came through the door. It was a trick that I was later to recommend to other harassed working mums, who otherwise risk unfair curtness towards children or partner. Many mums told me that they found the 'crossroads switch off' to be an invaluable tip.

Mrs T stayed with us for four years. We became the best of friends, indeed we kept up this friendship long after Mrs T retired from her child-care role. Additionally, we enjoyed the opportunities for social contact with her two adult offspring. Our first visit to her son and his family, when we stayed as guests in their Sussex home, proved to be an exciting and highly influential outing.

As a girl, Brighton, Hastings and Eastbourne had been the regular places of our family holidays, but I had not known rural

Sussex. Nor, before that visit, had I known that Mrs T's four grandchildren were adopted and of mixed race. One granddaughter was the same age and similar ethnicity to our own daughter. That memorable visit to Mrs T's family introduced us to life in a village on the edge of Ashdown Forest. My husband was captivated.

A couple of decades later, we three medical women friends had reached our fifties and were enjoying our London reunion. Anyone listening to our chatter about our respective jobs would find it hard to guess which path had been taken twenty years earlier! We were all back in full-time work as independent practitioners. Shirley had worked at a variety of jobs to fit in with her three children and the several family moves to accommodate her husband's career – including a permanent move overseas. At fifty, she was a specialist in venereal diseases ... the need for such clinics had not withered away. Stella, after her career break, had done a refresher course and was a tremendously busy and hard-working GP. I had worked my way back to full-time and, as a senior in our team, was contributing to policy development, teaching and audit. Yes, we certainly had learned to be expert jugglers.

Life had been very different for our own mothers, who had also managed home and 'career', the latter not necessarily in paid employment. When my Mum was a teenager, Grandpa had teasingly asked her, 'Do you want to be an M.A.?' Before she could enquire what that meant, he continued, 'You had better learn to be an M.A.M.A. and in the meantime you will have to earn your bread and butter.' Although she had a creative bent, a love of books and a longing to learn, my mother was despatched to secretarial college where, as she said, she learned to write shorthand at a speed much faster than any businessman she ever encountered could think! As a business secretary, she wrestled against many frustrations and feelings of futility. She became curious about how society worked, the issues around the General Strike, the scourge of unemployment and the rise of fascism – which was how she met my father.

A leaflet had been dropped through the letterbox of Grandpa's home: '*Give a welcome to the Hunger Marchers*'. My mother went down to the nearby Vicarage Hall in Stamford Hill – after all, her grandmother had slipped out of her home to hear Keir Hardie speak! My mother stood by the door, self-conscious of her tailored suit and her pale, empty hands. A young man, wearing the striped jacket of the doctor's 'uniform' of the time, thrust a bowl of antiseptic into those pale hands, commanding, 'Here you, take this. Don't slop it and follow me.' They did the round of sore and blistered feet, and thus, my parents began their life's journey together. Later, following him down miles and miles of hospital corridors on the continent, notebook and pencil at the ready, prepared to write down quotations, commentaries, statistics, she learned to be grateful for her ability to write prize-winning rapid shorthand.

I think of her as I sit at this computer with its miracles of cut and paste, copy, spell check. She would sit in our 'front room' (Dad's study), typing away as we came in from school, trying to complete the chapter before Dad came home from work. He would arrive with a bundle of papers exclaiming, 'Look at this! These figures have got to be included and we will have to expand the middle section.' Mum would sigh, as that meant a total re-type. I remember too, how inky we all got with the Gestetner roller-printer. Page by page we would roll out our nuclear disarmament leaflets through the ink block. Those memories haunt me now when I use font, boxes and automated layout to give emphasis to the written word and produce copies by computer printout at any size and in any number I wish. This, together with e-mail and Powerpoint, revolutionised my last years at work, enhancing teaching, communication with team contacts and exchange of clinical information in an unbelievable way.

Turning back once again to the Swinging Sixties, while we young people were pursuing our grant-aided academic training, Harold Wilson proudly introduced the Open University. 'Education, education, education,' was not such an original clarion call for

New Labour. Mum, then in her fifties, was among the first to enrol in the OU. She successfully graduated with a sociology degree, but believed she had learned more in the University of Life than ever she could in academic study. Her life of wide interests rested firmly on the home support provided by her own mother, my grandmother. We always took Granny's many skills and achievements for granted. Not only did she play a major role in the daily shopping, cooking and feeding of our family of seven, in the days before supermarkets, frozen foods and microwave, Granny also knitted endless jerseys, sewed and embroidered. She was bilingual, a regular reader and she sang German and Yiddish songs to us. Above all she emanated a gentleness and caring love. She could not bear strife and quarrelling. Perhaps that was the greatest legacy she gave us.

What of today's career girls? Educational, work and income opportunities have expanded in ways my generation could not have imagined and with unforeseen results. In my mother's generation, women gave up work on marriage. In mine, most gave up work on having children. Today many mothers of young children continue full-time work using child-care support. However, it is estimated that one in three women of child-bearing age today will choose not to have children. When I discussed this with a Spanish friend, a teacher, and told him that the average number of children per British woman is now below replacement rate at 1.6, he laughed at me.

'Well, here in Spain, yes in our Catholic country, it is around 0.6!'

Considering the five generations of women in my family whom I have known through stories told or actual experience, behind the change from my great-grandmother's brood of eight to today's women choosing none, lies a tremendous cultural revolution. What would Charles Bradlaugh and Annie Besant think if they were with us now? The contraceptive technique that they had recommended was the use of vaginal sponges – not an effective method. What would they say about our assisted reproduction techniques from artificial insemination to in vitro fertilisation (test tube babies)? What would they say about surrogate motherhood? Yes, the business of having children remains full of contradictions and difficult decisions. Our slogan of the '60s, *Every child a wanted child*, is still far from being achieved, and while today high-earning women do have a range of choices, what of the really hard-working mums whom we met at the clinics?

Chapter Fourteen

Changing Family Life

In the 1870s educated women campaigned for access to higher education, the opportunity to work as doctors, open information on contraception and for the vote. In the 1970s, feminists who were demanding control over their own fertility and lives, adopted the slogan *Our Bodies, Our Selves*. They argued for abortion on demand, free contraception and the extension of women's cancer-detection services. Women worked at self-empowerment. In small groups women used mirrors to become more familiar with their own intimate anatomy. The aim was to raise self-awareness and to be informed when meeting health professionals. (What would Elizabeth Garrett Anderson think of that!) The hunger for greater autonomy and independence animated the challenge of feminists of the '70s both at home and at work: why not have free state nurseries and wages for housework? Women needed equal educational opportunities and equal pay for equal work – the average woman's wages stood at 40% of the average man's. There was a demand for independent control over income: why should women declare their earnings on their husband's tax forms? Why were women barred from signing credit agreements or taking out mortgages? And why did women constitute only 5% of Members of Parliament? As a young woman of the '70s, I may have been living in rural Sussex, but I too wanted to find out more and, with curiosity, joined the debate in a Women's Consciousness Raising Group in Lewes.

We had a great time. I was still into singing and acting, so we created a stage performance about the women's struggle in the nineteenth and twentieth centuries using poems, letters, quotations and songs: my husband kindly did the singing for us. Titled *Presumptuous Girls*, we had a packed house and highly responsive audience in Lewes and the chance, much later, of a London performance.

In the meantime what had been happening inside family life? During my years at the Camden Town clinic, we had seen the struggle of deserted mothers raising up to half a dozen children or more. While formal divorce was increasing among middle-class families, desertion had been the more common experience of our unsupported mothers in rented accommodation or council flats. Divorce was costly, as was the maintenance paid by fathers who kept in touch with their children. Throughout the '70s, we saw the increase in desertion by fathers and were not surprised when the government introduced the Child Support Agency with power to chase up non-contributing absent fathers. In the mid-70s less than 10% of families were headed by lone parents, and almost all were mothers. Lone mothers were struggling to meet basic needs, never mind the emotional needs of their children – hence the Court Report's recommendation of more help for the million children growing up in one-parent families. On our Camden Town patch we had seen many of these children growing up strongly independent and spirited, heedless of rules and authority figures. We had referred the mums to the Child Guidance Clinic – as it was then called – a bus ride away at the local large teaching hospital. Waiting lists were long, and few of our mothers kept even the first appointment; follow-up ones were rarely kept. This was the drive behind our request for an Opportunity Class to offer help for the children within their school. Many of the lone parenting mothers were buoyant and cheerful and had the support of older women in their extended families. Others were subdued and we did not know how to encourage confidence. This was in the days before Erin Pizzey's refuge for battered wives in Chiswick stirred recognition of the problem of domestic violence. It took a further twenty years before the notion 'Zero Tolerance for Domestic Violence' was adopted as the proper stance.

By the early '70s, I had met many families where fathers had abandoned the children with no offer of future contact. One day, however, I was taken aback when a father, attending his daughter's school medical, thumped the desk heavily with his fist. He raged against his wife, who had walked out and left him with their ten-year-old daughter and six-year-old son. I felt dreadfully shocked. I was shocked by his publicly expressed anger, in front of the head-teacher, school nurse, welfare worker and myself. I was profoundly shocked to think that a mother could walk out on her own children. Well, what an innocent I was! By the end of my working years, I continued to be affected by similar departures, but habituation removed that earlier element of astonishment. Many of us professionals were indeed innocent – but not all of us. I have worked with women colleagues who have experienced violence in their own families of origin, or current marriages; women who, in the intimacy of our common work, have shared their own anguish, relating to conflict, desertion or sick partners. Whilst I myself was no stranger to grief, I still had much to learn.

Amongst the adolescents I saw at the Camden Town Family Clinic, I clearly recall a teenage girl who prattled on about her half-sister and her step-sister. Although I had regularly attended Dr Balint's voluntary sessions, that was in the early '60s when issues around reconstituted families just did not arise. I had to ask this girl what she meant by 'step' and 'half'. How strange that seems now! When trying to understand what was going on inside a family, we had been taught to draw a family tree, preferably covering three generations, tracing the influences between grandparents, parents and children. We could then reflect on the forces that were acting on troubled children. It was around the late '70s that we abandoned family trees and started to sketch family clusters. In these we could sketch the dynamics in the family of origin where the target child might be the younger of two. We could draw the dynamics in the mother's reconstituted family where this younger child might acquire younger half-siblings and become the second of four. On the fortnightly visit to the father's new home, the child might revert to being the youngest again, to a group of five children with the next eldest only a couple of months ahead and who might even be in the same class at school.

These observations do not mean that I believe tortured adults should remain locked in conflict for the sake of the children. Nor does it mean that lone parents should retain that lonely state. Many families have created greater stability and happiness through the process of change and family reconstitution. However, we were seeing the troubled children who presented with physical symptoms, educational failure, social difficulties or, most usually, combinations of these. Our job was to ascertain the health and developmental needs of the child and, through close working with the schools, to devise programmes of support involving the parents. Dialogue and partnership with parents was imperative, as it is the parents who provide the continuing influences in the child's life. We health and education staff only become temporarily involved during periods of acute distress. However, while it is the parents who, in their best judgement, make the decisions about family life, it is the children who have to learn to live with the outcomes.

Early in my career, I met teenagers who were articulate about family change, how they felt about this and about the various adults adopting parenting roles towards them. Later, we had to learn to help under-fives cope with change. This required careful and sensitive observation of very young children and close working with parents and nursery class teachers, and, for some youngsters, with speech therapists. Among the hardest problems which emerged towards the end of my career were situations where fathers who had deserted very young children, under the age of three, reappeared after a substantial gap with a new family, wanting access to the earlier-born children. Such cases went to court, bringing havoc to the mother and new partner, who may have offered unconditional love and caring as step-father. It is a truism that our knowledge and perspective were constantly challenged by change.

During my training, the psychiatric support services for children were delivered from 'Child Guidance Clinics'. Appropriate advice to parents could enable them to better guide the child to more stable and contained behaviours. During my Public Health course, I was startled by a lecture by Dr John Howells, Director of the Institute for Family Psychiatry in Ipswich. His thesis now seems elementary and crystal clear. He suggested that the child, by virtue of immaturity, would be the weakest member of the family. In situations of tension or overt strife, the adults may be sophisticated enough to reveal the child's problems while concealing their own, either through denial or deliberate intent. The weakest member of the family, the disturbed child, becomes the marker of family instability and dysfunction. Years after I had already adopted the name Family Clinic for our referral clinics, the Child Guidance Clinics were renamed Family Consultation Centres, thus reflecting the change in approach. I would refer on about 5% of our caseload to these clinics, which were led by consultant child psychiatrists.

In 1995, as part of the Health of the Nation project, a handbook on helping children and adolescents with mental health problems was published by the Department of Health. This spelled out the four tiers of service provision, with GPs, health visitors and school nurses being in the front line and community paediatricians like myself being in the second tier. After 30 years of such work it was gratifying to have it officially recognised. The specialist child psychiatric service teams were the third tier and day units and other highly specialised units provided the fourth. Parents would commonly approach the first-tier professionals with their concerns; 75% of my referrals came in equal parts from GPs, health visitors and school nurses. We, unusually, were an open-access clinic so the other new families came as self-referrals having heard about us through their friends, from teacher recommendation or from one of my parents' evenings at playgroup or school.

In the late '70s, most of our referred children lived in intact families. By the time I retired, most were in restructured homes. Latterly, I have noticed how stories about restructured families have become popular in children's reading books. The wicked stepmother of my girlhood reading, consumed by jealousy of her husband's lovely daughter, has been swept away. Instead, books now centralise the child's view. Young girls writhe at their mother's embarrassing attempts at dating boyfriends. Boys and girls squirm over the antics of step-parents, are scathing in their judgements and the stepfather can be disparagingly dubbed 'the monster'. Fictional foster children give a mouthful of abuse about foster parents, and their love/hate relationship with social workers animates the pages. This shift in perception and power base from adult to child makes such books highly popular with young readers.

Of course our clinic did not just serve children in restructured families. Many intact families had their own pressing concerns about their children which derived from developmental delays, unexplained educational failure, children's physical ill-health and disability, sensory loss and unusual behavioural characteristics. Moreover, concerns about children often centred on the need to help them cope with adult misfortune: parents with cancer, depression or other challenging health problems. Over the years we increasingly received requests for help around issues of child protection and we always had engagement with parents of adopted or fostered children. It is into these areas that this story will travel later, but first a look back at our removal to Sussex.

Chapter Fifteen

New Vistas and New Perspectives

During his seven years in Hackney, my husband became convinced of the need to work at the development of whole communities rather than just the needs of minority groups. The trip to the Sussex village to meet Mrs T's family had captured his imagination. When in 1974 a job came up in Community Development work in Lewes, he decided to apply and was duly appointed. I was bitterly torn about leaving London. It was in the north London area that I had been to school, trained as a doctor and done most of my post-graduate study. I loved that Camden Town clinic and the teaching in the schools, and I was also a visiting lecturer at a London professional training centre. The television work was an occasional but absorbing interest. Besides, Grandpa was nearly ninety, he was still well, active and working in his Indian import business. We visited him regularly on Sunday afternoons. He took much pleasure in his great-grandchildren. Additionally, our lovely Victorian home was within pushchair distance of some half-dozen of my women friends who were also mothers. After my morning clinic, we would meet up and think nothing of the five-mile tramp, pushing the kids in their buggies across Hampstead Heath, where they could play and we could chat and enjoy afternoon tea. However, the thought of the country while the children were young also held a particular allure. I owe the genesis of that allure to my parents' political awareness.

In the late 1930s, my parents had been acutely conscious of the imminence of war. Having closely followed the events of the Spanish Civil War and aware of the terrible impact of the aerial bombing of Guernica when 1600 civilians died in the three-hour raid, they determined to escape from the expected air raids on the capital. My father sold his general practice and was drafted as an industrial doctor to the factories of the Midlands. My mother, together with her parents and my toddler brother, moved out to a village in Buckinghamshire. That was where I was born. We stayed there throughout the war, returning to London after VE day, when I was five years old. Thus whereas I had been taken from my country living to the great city when I was five, we made the reverse journey with our own daughter when she reached that age. I hold one very clear and bright image from those early years in Buckinghamshire: a field of sparkling pale-yellow cowslips, a path running down through these to the brook where large cows grazed. My childish mind held a confused image of the large shapes of the cows and the name of the flower.

We searched Lewes for a Victorian home but these were few and far between as the nineteenth-century development in Brighton had usurped growth in the County Town. Well, we argued, as we are going to experience a complete change in our way of living, let's do this thoroughly. We were fortunate to find our seventeenth-century farmhouse, nestling below the Downs in a small village just outside Lewes. Having struggled eastward across heavy London traffic for seven years to reach his Hackney office, my husband was bowled over by the five-minute run up a country road to his Lewes workplace. Our farmhouse was also a bonus for our London friends, who would regularly visit us with their young families and together we would explore the wonderful countryside and coast. Mum came to stay for a few days mid-week on a regular basis. The children looked forward to their after-school outing with Granny – and we to our chance of an evening babysitter. Mum even managed to bring my Grandpa, just once, to see our country home. He gazed up at the hills, at the cows on the farm, the pigs and free-range hens alongside us. He sat silently in our front room looking up at the low beamed ceiling. With a reflective smile, he mused, '...and to think we were eight children in one bed!' Adding with zest, 'If I were to have my life again, I would live in the country.'

Our remaining times with Grandpa that winter were on our trips to London. He died the following spring. For all his early deprivations, Grandpa had remained generally fit and active in his mature years and was even working on the day he died. He had spent only his last three days in bed with bronchitis. His departure, six months after our move, felt like another closure on my London life.

We busily threw our energies into our Sussex life. I spent the early weeks settling our daughter into her school and our son into his village playgroup. Our two-year-old son soon fell in with a crowd of little boys, including a lovely Japanese chum whose father was here on a sabbatical year at the University of Sussex. The family were near neighbours and I used to take our son over to play with Jiro, while his mother and I, without a common language, would look at picture books together. Because of my long training, most of my friends already had little families before we had even our first baby. Our daughter had arrived into a community of friends, providing ready playmates for her. Our arrival in Sussex was a cultural challenge for us all. I met our daughter at the village school and asked her to show me the girls she played with. Saying hello to two infant-aged sisters, I asked, 'Where is your Mummy? I would like to meet her.' (This was long before the stranger/danger campaign.) They ran ahead across the village green with us in tow. We arrived at their home on the modern housing estate. Their mother came to the door. I smiled, introducing myself, saying, 'Our daughters seem to be friends so I thought that I'd come and say hello.'

'Gee that's swell,' came a distinctly American voice. 'My husband is here on sabbatical. I've been in this village a whole month and you're my first caller.'

We had been there just over a week!

Gradually, we did make friends. I found two mothers who were each willing to do a day's exchange caring with me, collecting the children after playgroup and school, so I could restart part-time work. We were invited to a mid-summer fancy-dress party. All the men came in boiler suits with very crude logos attached, for they were the 'Rude Mechanicals'. Most of the women arrived as Titania, looking like something out of a classical white ballet. I too, went as the Fairy Queen, but in my aberrant fashion, had streaked my face blue, my hair straggled freely and I wore a ragged green leaf-form robe. Guests would approach me and ask, '...and what do you do?'

Behind my blue mask I would proudly reply, 'I am a mother, and in my spare time, I do a few medical clinics.'

In our spare time we were soon taking part in village theatricals and musical performances. In the Christmas pantomime, my husband sang the Demon King. Our son and his mates were all the little demons and they cheered so loudly each time the Demon King came on stage that the Fairy Queen was quite sidelined. Being a social work colleague, she took it in good part.

Living in a university area meant that there were always sabbatical families from overseas in the village. However, as an ethnically different family, we found that we stood out in a way that had been irrelevant in London. I usually wore my long dark hair firmly pinned in a bun. People took us for an all-Indian family. The children received a tea invitation from an octogenarian retired teacher who wanted to meet 'the little Indian children'. My daughter's teacher asked me when I had come to Britain. I was startled, thinking that she had noticed I was Jewish. She was amazed when I replied, 'Oh, I am fourth generation. My great-grandfather came in the 1880s.' It was only later that I realised the misconception.

There was no misconception in the minds of those who stuck KEEP SUSSEX WHITE posters on our gate. Unfortunately, this occurred during one of my mother's regular visits to stay with us. It brought back sharp memories for her of the swastikas that had been daubed on my father's north London surgery doors way back in the late 1930s. In the early '70s, there was a trickle of removal into the county of ethnic minority families – mainly those who were setting up Indian or Chinese restaurants. Looking around the rows of heads at the village school assembly, I was surprised how very blond they all seemed. Amongst more than a hundred heads, you could count the dark-haired children on fewer than the fingers of both hands. The only other ethnically different children were black children from outside, placed by adoption in white homes. That is, of course, another story ... one that also needs to be told.

Chapter Sixteen

Returning to Work:
Contrasts and Echoes

My husband was travelling widely across the county, drives which, after the London rat runs, gave him endless pleasure. He was gaining information about the needy areas of the county and we were surprised to find that some of the wards in Brighton, Hove and Hastings ranked with the deprivation we had seen in Inner London. Shortly after our arrival, I had a routine visit from the health visitor. In those days, all new families transferring in with under-fives had such a routine health-check call. My new health visitor settled down in our farmhouse kitchen with a cup of tea. Surprised to learn of my speciality, she plied me with questions about my London job. Amongst other matters, I told her about our family clinics.

'Why,' she announced, 'we have had such a clinic here in Lewes for the past five years, aimed at supporting mothers with pre-schoolchildren.'

She continued to explain that she worked at the clinic with Dr F. but this doctor was approaching retirement and there was no other doctor in the team available to take the work on. The clinic would probably be closed and she much regretted this. Would I be interested in the clinic? Prompted by this information, and somewhat earlier than I had intended, I wrote a 'Dear Doctor' letter to the Head of the Child Health Services. Imagine my surprise when I received a 'Dear Sonya' reply, for not only had the doctor in question been in my year on the Public Health course, we had even worked together on our 'Health Education in School' project group.

Aware of the problems my husband was discovering, when I met my ex-fellow student at County Hall, I applied to work in eastern Brighton or the port town of Newhaven. I was told that these towns had plenty of doctors but the rural areas were desperately short. It was agreed that I could take on the Lewes Family Clinic – I subsequently worked there for twenty-six years, extending the age group seen up to sixteen years and, latterly, running two sessions a week. I was asked to take on a rural patch comprising two small towns and a run of villages. One town had an army camp with fathers doing a tour of duty in Northern Ireland. The mothers and the children had experienced repeated moves and I would find children who needed health and educational support. There was also a Traveller community with unmet health needs. A new unit for hearing-impaired children was being planned within one of the mainstream primary schools. Moreover a residential school for 'maladjusted children' was opening in the second town and I would serve the children there. Both towns were designated growth towns. Together with the Lewes Family Clinic, this programme would give me scope to extend my interests and would certainly be a contrast to my London experience. I signed up, uncertain of what the future held. I stayed in that post, gradually increasing from half-time to almost full-time hours, before moving on fifteen years later when my own children approached the end of their schooling.

Before this rural experience, I had thought that my Balint-inspired approach had enabled me to learn a lot about our Camden families. What nonsense! The transience of contact, the pressures of numbers, the large and varied population we had served meant that I had only really skimmed the surface of family difficulties. Here in Sussex I was supported by school nurses who had always lived in their towns, who knew so much about the local families, inter-relations and connections, whose own children were attending the local schools and who knew the local politics. Even the permanent teaching staff in the schools were indeed 'permanent' and they too had a wealth of information about the families and the community. It all felt so different.

Shortly after I started this work, the Court Report *Fit for the Future* was published. Reviewing the health needs of children, it contained a raft of recommendations about improving the ways in which we delivered our services. High priority was given to the need to replace the rapid undress medical at school with a thorough health and developmental assessment six months before school entry in the privacy of the clinic. Planned support for school entry could be arranged for children with needs. I was asked to introduce this change at our clinics. Conferring with the health visitors, we gave four appointments to those with no known concerns at the start of the clinic, followed by longer appointments for one or two children with recognised needs. With parental consent, the outcome of assessment was shared with the head-teachers of the receiving schools. Support services were put in place and a review programme was planned. I gained an awareness of these families and their needs – those of the titled and tied cottages – that far surpassed my London work. I was most gratified when one of the head-teachers commented that not all the children I had spoken about had difficulties in his school, but all the children with difficulties were in the early-alert group and their support services were valued. I wrote up a report of 250 consecutive assessments, categorising the concerns raised by 80% of the parents. I was rebuffed by the academic reviewers. 'Of course, if a nice doctor somewhere asks parents nicely whether they have concerns about their children's health, the majority will seek advice. So what? Does that justify a doctor's time or make any difference?'

Whilst the Court Report had placed great importance on the value of the universal pre-school health assessment, this was gradually replaced by a targeted service. We doctors began to focus our attention only on the young children brought forward by health visitors and nursery teachers, while the school nurses conducted a general health care interview with the rest. Even this targeted approach has been further refined, with the school nurses taking responsibility for children for whom there are general concerns and the doctors seeing only those with the most specialised needs. Thirty years after the Court Report, the whole-population approach has been replaced by a focus on expressed or recognised need.

Throughout my work in the schools, I continued to meet many fine and dedicated teachers, sensitive to needy children, ready to seek help and concerned to arrange a network of care. This was as true of the town comprehensives as of the rural family-type small village schools, although the work style differed greatly. As the routine assessments vanished from the programme, our time was appropriately redirected towards helping troubled children. There was never a shortage of referrals. We started giving parents 'special' appointments at the end of the school day at the clinics. The number of 'specials' increased until we were running regular Family Clinics in all three towns. Some of these children found their way into our own special school, designated for 'maladjusted children' but latterly reclassified for the 'educationally and behaviourally disturbed'. At the same time, our special schools for the 'educationally subnormal' were renamed as schools for those with 'learning difficulties.' Perhaps there *is* something in a name!

Networking with colleagues was far easier in these rural communities than in London. I was asked to represent our medical department at the Nurses College in Brighton. I began to contribute to health visitor training in the assessment of the under-fives and held seminars on the newly introduced modular course for school nurses. Later, I took part in midwife training and on courses for 'sick children's nurses'. Through these contacts, I was able to have detailed discussions on service development with the nursing tutors and to have personal contact with the first-tier nurses who, following their training, were working widely across the county. Contacts with social workers, school psychologists and clinic psychiatrists were also easier and more personalised than in London. We had a local voluntary group of the National Children's Bureau (NCB) and colleagues from various disciplines would meet in Lewes on a monthly basis for a lecture or visit to some therapeutic establishment to learn about new developments. I soon found myself as the medical representative on the committee and chaired it for the last four years until its demise in the Thatcher era. Then, increasing staff cuts left those still in post so burdened with official evening meetings that they lacked the energy to support our voluntary group. I was very sorry to lose this forum.

One meeting of the local NCB group which challenged my learned concepts, was about children with Down's syndrome. Despite my earlier experience using intelligence tests on West Indian children in London schools for the educationally subnormal, I had undoubtedly been influenced by notions of the genetic nature of intelligence and the prediction of learning potential. Our lecturer presented studies of Down's syndrome children who, with supportive learning programmes, had been enabled to join their local primary schools and had mastered the ability to read. My notions of certainty were again shaken. Some years later, we received Virginia in one of our village schools, a school which also served the Traveller children. Clearly affected with the syndrome, Virginia was a most attractive child with green eyes, red curly hair and a most delightful manner. Her local primary school was in the town, but she joined the village school where she would be in smaller classes and where the teachers already ran a supportive literacy programme introduced to help the Traveller children for whom regular attendance was often difficult. We accepted Virginia for two years, however she surprised us with her marked progress. She stayed throughout her six years of primary schooling, learned to read and write, took part in school performances and was highly popular. That was another shock to my belief in the correctness of what I had been taught. A greater shock was yet to come, under the topic of child protection.

Chapter Seventeen

'Suffer Little Children'

From *Grimm's Fairy Tales* to *The Water Babies* and *David Copperfield*, images of neglected, abandoned and abused children wove their way through the pages of the voracious reading of my girlhood years. It still came as a terrible shock when, at medical school, we were shown X-ray images of babies and toddlers with multiple fractures and were told about the 'Battered Baby Syndrome'. The year was 1961 and the condition had just been newly described to the American Academy of Paediatrics.

Thankfully, through my four decades of practice I was never faced with a drastically beaten child in my case-load. Whenever I read the reports of brutal child deaths, I was haunted by the question of whether we would have done better in similar circumstances. I cannot recall any physically abused children during my time on the wards, but I well remember the first I saw at the Camden Town clinic.

Charlene was only six months old. Her young mother brought her to our well-baby clinic saying the child had toppled over and now would not move her right arm. On careful examination, I could feel the fracture across the middle part of the bone of her upper arm. I looked up at the mother to explain what we must do and suddenly noticed that the mother had a small bluish bruise above her left eyebrow.

'Oh dear,' I exclaimed. 'What has happened to you?'

'I was reaching to a high shelf for a biscuit tin and the tin slipped, just catching me above my eye.'

We made a sling for the baby and explained the arrangements we had made at the Casualty Department. After the clinic, my wise superintendent health visitor scolded me for my innocence. She knew the baby's father. Neither the injury to the mother nor to the baby had been accidental. She explained the routine for the action we must take. Charlene, with her fractured arm, was the most seriously physically abused child I ever saw. We did however see many slap marks and adult-inflicted bruises. One night, while bathing my own children, tired and irritated by my testy three-year-old son, I shamefully recall slapping him – another important lesson for me. Some thirty years later, while not outlawing all physical punishment, MPs have voted to outlaw abusive punishment that leaves grazes, scratches, bruises or causes mental harm. Whilst twelve other European countries have a total ban on hitting children, here, sadly, the parents' right to hit their children continues.

Far more common than physical assault was the emotional cruelty, neglect and humiliation meted out to children. Most of the children so abused were presented to us by health visitors and teachers. In London, one of our head-teachers told us of a little boy who used to blow into his hands and then stuff his clenched fists into his pockets just before going home from school. Asked why he did this, he painfully responded that he could not breathe at home. He needed the air from school. In the book *Children in Distress*, Alec Clegg, Chief Education Officer for the West Riding of Yorkshire, commented that for many children school was the therapy. Over the years, I have worked with many sensitive teachers who have comforted and supported unhappy children. Many infant school head-teachers have encouraged failing parents to take part in classroom fun activities and to join in class outings – experiences which can raise parental awareness and self-esteem.

I too worked on the mother rota at my children's playgroup and was a volunteer helper in their reception classes for four years. This again was an experience no lecture, seminar or case presentation could have conveyed.

I watched group interactions, childish spitefulness and unfairness unnoticed by the busy teacher. I saw bullying and the ways in which a child could be marginalised in incidents not seen by the teacher. I watched a teacher reach into a cupboard and hand a musical instrument to one of the more reserved children in the class. Another child snatched at this before the girl could receive it. The same pattern was repeated four or five times while the teacher was busily rummaging in the cupboard. When the teacher emerged from the cupboard and asked which children did not have an instrument, the shy girl was obliged to raise her hand. When the staff at my children's school became aware that I was the children's doctor at the Family Clinic, they suggested that I might like to do reading support with children in the class who were attending the clinic. Ensuring that my role would still be that of voluntary helper, I agreed. This too proved to be an invaluable lesson, adding a new dimension to my understanding of the child's difficulties and ways of relating to adults.

Back at the start of my work with young children, Matron at the Camden Day Nursery had lined up more than a dozen children for me to 'inspect' ears, nose, throat and chest on my morning visit. Conscious of my recent induction into assessing child development, I asked her to present only six children so that I could use my box of bricks and toys to give a full health and developmental assessment. By the time I had moved to Sussex, the ethos of the day nursery had given place to family centres run by Social Service Departments, offering support to mothers and children. Over the time I worked in Sussex, there was a push to increase nursery education, a push which took over twenty years to achieve results. During my last decade of working, I covered a nursery school serving a deprived area. The staff selected 40% of entrants for the evaluation of various health and developmental concerns. Behavioural difficulties reflecting family pressures were the commonest concern behind referral. All these children had been carefully appraised by their teachers and nearly all of the parents accepted the invitation to meet the doctor at the school. Where parents needed more time, we could offer appointments at the Family Clinic.

Like other therapists, we had the opportunity to explore the children's feelings through their drawings. Amongst my collection, I have pictures reflecting physical problems of vision, heart function or bone fractures, drawn by the child while the parent had been discussing the problems with me. A lonely, only child drew a picture of himself fishing with his friends while his mother was talking about their isolated living condition. A boy with markedly poor coordination drew an animated image of himself playing football. The boy with poor concentration, listening skills and balance drew a striking image of different coloured lines and curves in an apparently random but bold pattern. A girl with eczema obsessively coloured every last scrap of the paper. A highly nervous girl who needed to frequently empty her bladder, drew 'Mr Mouse'. The children also drew their near familiars, including 'the bad mummy who won't let me talk', a remarkable picture of granny with a loving smile, a brother and sister cheek to cheek. Some children utilised cartoon images to illustrate their thoughts. A five-year-old girl drew a cartoon of herself with bags under the eyes and told me it was herself 'feeling unhappy 'cos of bad dreams and monsters coming onto my head and bees'.

A most striking set of cartoon characters came from an isolated ten-year-old girl who was unhappy and failing at school. She had been referred by her teacher. The mother told me a painful story centred on her older daughter. She explained how, following the break-up of the family, she and the younger daughter had sought comfort with a distant male relative, who then became the mother's new partner. The tensions and conflict emanated from the adults. The younger daughter had been marginalised and felt overwhelmed. I sat with this girl and talked with her about her life at school, her interests and what she enjoyed. As she said she liked drawing, I asked her to bring one on her next visit. The picture was three cartoon bears in a row. The first was small and unhappy. His balloon read: nobody loves me, I feel ill. The second was a very large sad bear saying: the doctor loves me, I feel ill. The last was a small happy bear with the caption: everybody loves me, I feel well.

Many distressed children desperately need space to express their wishes and feelings. This need became enshrined in the 1989 Children Act. Just as the women's refuges of the '70s had opened public debate on the silent topic of domestic violence, so too did creating space for the child's voice reveal, among other concerns, the misery of child sexual abuse. This topic was billed for our in-service training day. The specialist team from London's Great Ormond Street Hospital was visiting Brighton and all child health doctors and nurses were expected to attend. My school nurse and I finished our morning session at the clinic. Over sandwiches, we discussed the families we had seen and planned action to take matters forward. Then, with definite scepticism, we talked of the afternoon's coming seminar. Yes, we knew about the molestation of young teenage girls and their particular vulnerability to male relatives and to certain step-fathers who had intimate access within the home. We could not believe that pre-pubertal children were vulnerable in that way. Together we travelled to the post-graduate centre and sat noisily among our colleagues.

Dr Bentovin was introduced and began his presentation. We were soon listening attentively to the evidence and statistics. Case presentations provoked thoughts about families we knew. We felt an uneasy sense of recognition and consciousness of our own denial. We were horrified by the devastating effects of disclosure on the families. The number of men who went on to self-harm was particularly depressing. From that time on, we knew we would have to be alert and involved. In fact, children rarely disclosed to us. In the schools, teachers became more reactive to inappropriate behaviour and would discuss this with us. We would

107

plan a way of approaching the parents. After completing investigative work at specialist centres, affected families would come to the local clinic and we would work at further coping strategies, always working closely with Social Services. Case conferences increasingly punctuated our routines. At first these were attended by the professionals only: social workers, teachers, doctors and nurses. In this closed forum there was always the sneaking suspicion of unfair censure, however objective we tried to be. Later, parents were invited to take part. Their presence certainly influenced our manner of reporting and sharing concerns and how we phrased assessments. It felt to be a far better way of working – however, particular circumstances remain when it is appropriate to meet without the parents.

Our GPs rarely found time to attend; I was often the sole medical representative. As our medical work pressures increased, the school nurse or health visitor acted as sole health member, reporting back both to the GPs and to the Child Health doctors. In recent years, complaints against doctors working in child protection have been increasing, although the vast majority of these are not upheld. Doctors are becoming unwilling to take on this work and, as I write, 30% of paediatric posts with the duty to lead in child protection are unfilled.

My clinical work threw up innumerable encounters with suffering children. Meantime, I also read the literature from voluntary groups campaigning against child workers, child soldiers, child torture, child prostitutes, even child slaves. Such readings gave a sense of huge despair. My first trip to India brought me face to face with the misery of child hunger, disease and dispossession.

The Court Report had said: *the rearing of the young is the fundamental issue in human society.* Against that precept, where, I wonder, do we measure?

Chapter Eighteen

We Travel to India

In 1968, the year after the fiasco of our Polish camping trip, we finally made our first visit together to India. We had already been married for six years and while I had never met my in-laws, we had been exchanging regular letters. (Indeed, some forty years later, I still send my fortnightly letter, now by email, to my widowed mother-in-law.) I was anxious to make a good impression. One of my close girl friends, a health visitor who also worked at the Camden Town clinic, accompanied me to a lively 1960s boutique just up the road from our clinic. We chose a silk dress with a sleeveless, close bodice and full skirt with crazy psychedelic patterns in pink, red and orange. The second choice was a more formal fawn linen dress of similar cut. The hemline of both dresses was well above my knees. We all wore mini-dresses both for work and leisure. I should have known better. Grandpa had already teasingly scolded us for our minis.

'Don't you know,' he jocularly warned, 'when I was young, my heart would beat faster when I glimpsed an ankle! You can't understand men if you walk around like that.'

I had smiled and hugged him.

Given my job with its school duties, I could only take extended, unpaid leave during the school summer holidays. I had loved the heat in Italy and was totally relaxed about going to India in July and August. In addition to the exorbitant cost of plane travel in the '60s (our two return tickets equalled a year of my salary), long-haul flights were unknown. We had four touch-downs on our way to Bombay. I had never flown before and was wildly apprehensive. On the first short hop, we hit such turbulence that the air-hostesses could not serve the meal, passengers were sick, and pillows and blankets tumbled from the overhead open luggage rack on top of us. I kept thinking of Piglet in Kanga's pouch crying out '...if this is flying, I shall never really take to it.' I needed a sleeping pill before I could face going back on board for the second lap.

Before reaching Bombay, I had changed from jeans into my little pink silk dress and duly came happily through to meet the family. The heat hit me, as if I had walked into an oven, the crowds overwhelmed me and the noisy chaos was totally alarming. My mother-in-law firmly held my left hand as we were driven from the airport towards Bombay; with my right hand I was repeatedly tugging at my skirt hem to draw it over my knees. The following day, my sister-in-law took me out to buy a couple of pairs of attractive churidah/chamize sets (tunic/trousers), complete with delightful silver buttons sporting dangling bells and the chunni (scarf). Thus attired, and with shiuli flowers in my hair and a silver bird hairpin in my bun, when walking around the colourful, scented and noisy markets, I was as captivated as any British '60s hippy.

During that first visit, my parents-in-law arranged a special trip for us all, including my husband's sister. The five of us were to fly to Aurungabad to see the ancient cave paintings in Ajanta and the spectacular carved temples with their reclining Buddha at Ellora. This was the stuff of E.M. Forster! We arrived at Bombay Domestic Terminal and walked across the tarmac to mount the steps into our little plane. It looked so fragile. Just before take-off, I gripped my arm-rests and closed my eyes. Ma roared with laughter.

'This is the Doctor-Memsahib we were so nervous of meeting? She doesn't drink, she doesn't smoke, she doesn't wear make-up and she is scared of flying!'

Over those six weeks we travelled to stay with relatives in Delhi, Lucknow, Varanasi and Kolkata where I met the grandparents. We ended this grand tour with a two-day train journey back to Bombay from Kolkata. Whilst in Varanasi I had phoned Grandpa's business associates. We were invited to have dinner with the family. Out of courtesy, I wore a sari although I have neither the grace, posture nor gestures to carry it off. My husband accompanied me to this Muslim household. There, prominently displayed on the wall, was a photo of Grandpa, the frame garlanded with fresh marigolds. We were invited to visit the workshop. I was startled, thinking at first sight that they employed all the one-armed lepers of Varanasi. Then I realised that these men, who were sitting cross-legged on the floor with a loom across their laps, were pushing the needle vertically downward with their right hands and returning it with their left hands, which were concealed beneath the frame.

We adjourned for our meal. I was the only female at the table. We were served by young men of the family. I was accustomed to eating a mainly vegetarian diet with much rice and potatoes. Here I was offered huge plates of meat. As usual, I ate with my hands. Following this feast, I was invited to visit the women's quarter. A young male relative accompanied me. The women, in their tunic/trouser suits, covered their heads, turned to look at me, giggled and turned away again. I was staring at the multiple sets of large gold earrings that they wore in their ear-lobes. They were staring hard at me and then, through the young man, asked, 'Do all the women in London wear a sari?'

While in Varanasi, a medical member of the business family took me round the teaching hospital. Our ward round was shocking. Walking from bed to bed, with my guide telling me the various diagnoses, was a disturbing experience. So too was the walk along the external path leading to the operating theatres – for goats were busily rummaging in the rubbish beside the notice reading, *Masks and gowns only beyond this point.*

I was introduced to Dr Varma, head of the Public Health Department. What an encounter! This animated man explained how each medical student was allocated to one family from a poor district of 1700 people, of whom 40% were under fifteen and 70% were illiterate. The student had to monitor and log the health and disease experiences of the family over the next three years. Students were positively barred from offering financial help, but were actively involved in community health schemes, whether this meant digging latrines or accompanying people for mass chest X-ray. What an eye-opener that must have been, a far greater shake-up than our student home visits with the midwives.

Undoubtedly, the romance of India captivates the imagination. The wonders of the evening boat ride passing sunken temples at Varanasi, the splendour of the Taj Mahal and the beauty of the many Delhi monuments and those at Lucknow were all quite overwhelming. Overwhelming in another way was to be offered delicacies and quantities of food I could never manage to eat in a country with rampant under-nutrition. I visited privileged homes where the bevy of servants sparked images in my mind of the genteel life of Victorian Britain. As a doctor, it was impossible to ignore the people around me. In the city building sites, I saw women balancing bricks on their heads as they ascended the bamboo scaffolding. I saw pairs of women in the countryside lifting water from a canal to an irrigation ditch, using banana leaves. Walking through the streets, noting the stigma of diseases that I only knew from textbooks, I felt as if I was in our Pathology Museum. The under-nourishment, deformities and untreated conditions were shocking, as was the sight of so many young polio victims, some ten years after I had received my first polio vaccination. I was mortified by the begging. I could not look away, neither could I make eye contact. Back home, I remember crying uncontrollably as I tried to talk about these impressions with my friends.

I have been visiting India regularly over the past thirty-five years and thankfully so much has improved. Gross disease is no longer so evident, polio is almost eliminated, people are taller and stronger. There is ample evidence of mechanised advance in town and country but, unsurprisingly, dire poverty continues alongside flyovers, air conditioning and luxurious five-star hotels.

Just before my retirement in 2000, I visited my health visitor friend who was doing voluntary maternity and child welfare work with a non-government organisation among nomadic people in the foothills of the Himalayas. We arranged to go Moosorie, to the summer resort of the Maharajah of Nabha, now a hotel. The rapidly ascending drive up from Dehra Dun was stunning. The mountainside was criss-crossed with tracks and whatever land could be terraced was growing rice and vegetables. I wondered what had driven the British to ascend to such rugged heights in the 1820s? Until one has experienced the punishment of Delhi summer heat, forty degrees day after day, barely relieved by the fall to thirty degrees at night, one can only feel aghast at such a feat.

Today, at Moosorie, the Maharajah's palace is managed by an Indian hotel chain named Claridges. Not only does the company assume the British name for the business, but also the traditional British style for their service. The bungalow guest rooms open onto a semi-circular veranda, ringing a charming small garden which leads to the main residence built on a rocky outcrop to take advantage of any breeze. There, the Maharajah once offered hospitality. Today, the bearers still dress in military-style, belted tunics. The musty, disinfectant-smelling interior, heavy with ruched pelmets and looped-back curtains, displays a large portrait of the turbaned and moustached smiling Maharajah himself – resplendent in military tunic complete with epaulettes and lanyard. Meantime, affluent Indian women in western jeans and trainers glance away from we two British women who are traipsing around in flowing churidah/chamize outfits complete with chunni.

Is globalisation pervading modern India? Certainly I saw images of businesswomen fronting the magazines. I saw earnest men and women in trainers, jogging pants and wearing head-sets, pounding the concrete peripheral path that now weaves around my favourite Delhi garden with the great mausoleums of the fifteenth-century

113

Lodhi emperors. Throughout Kolkata, the little kiosks which crop up repeatedly in crowded thoroughfares announce that in addition to internal and external phone calls, they now also provide e-mail and internet. However, observing the still widely prevalent arduous manual labour, or experiencing the hierarchical bureaucracy, or listening to the stories my health visitor friend told of her work, leads me to believe that it will take far more than globalisation to change the culture of living amidst this heat and this dust.

Chapter Nineteen

White Sussex, Black Children

In the streets, markets and public gardens of India, I had experienced the self-consciousness of being the only European in the bustling throng. Scanning the heads at assembly in our children's village school revealed serried ranks of blond children. Walking across the playgrounds of the Sussex schools I visited regularly, the same sea of blond heads caught my eye. This contrasted with my walks across the Camden school playgrounds, where I had seen children from all parts of the world. In the 1970s, of the dozen or so ethnic minority children whom I saw at our family clinics, all were placed with white families – and my estimate is that nearly all such children so placed in our patch of this rural county at that time were referred to some specialist helping agency. In rural Sussex, ethnic minority children were seen as different by their classmates and were highly noticeable in the classroom, particularly when some focus of misdemeanour attracted the teacher's attention.

The adolescents were more able to find words to reflect their feelings. Stuart was a lively-looking, black, fifteen-year-old lad who attended a comprehensive school serving a rural town of 20,000 and the surrounding villages. He was restless, disaffected and rebellious both in class and with his foster family. At the clinic, with great animation he expressed his frustration.

'I'd rather be back in Lambeth hanging round the railings with me mates, than hanging around here where there ain't even no railings to hang around.'

Two black sisters, fostered together with a very caring couple, also attended his school. Their feelings of exclusion could not be soothed. The elder had lovely eyes and a tall, strong figure. Her teachers recognised her depression and her feelings of being on the edge of her class. She accepted her referral.

'I had a boyfriend,' she said wistfully, 'but he told me he couldn't go out with me any longer, 'cos if he did, no white girl would ever go out with him again.'

By contrast, in London, when the young half-Indian daughter of our friends had been told by her classmate that it was a pity she was brown, for although she was very pretty nobody would love her, she had confidently replied, 'But my Mummy is brown and my Daddy loves her.'

Following a Christmas trip to their grandparents in Kolkata, our two children returned to school with a summer tan. Both were teased. 'Don't play with them, you'll get the Brownie-touch.' Our seven-year-old son was very upset. Their father spoke with the head-teacher and offered to do a slide show – not the images I was collecting for my Public Health talks, but the white tiger in Kolkata Zoo, palaces, fortresses, strange cacti. The children loved it. They were invited to write an individual letter of thanks stating which picture they liked the best. The white tiger had indeed been the most popular slide. The class-cred of our son went soaring up!

Our young, fostered, black children did not have the language to explain their feelings, nor that kind of intimate support. A distressed Nathaniel, aged eight and the only black child in his village school, stood on the grass hummock near the centre of the playground and urinated as boldly and as far as he could.

Understandably, such inner turbulence held back learning. Just as black children had been over-represented in the London schools for the 'educationally subnormal' in the '60s, so too I found a high use of child mental health services and schools for the 'maladjusted' by ethnic minority children in our county in the '70s. This again raises questions of perception and, even more importantly, of cultural issues. Meantime, the fate of fostered black children was being hotly debated in London: a drive was under way to find black foster families for black children. Was this a racist idea or was it meant to protect the identity and interests of the child? I went up to London join the debate at a medical conference.

'Surely,' I declared from the floor, 'it is unfair to spearhead change by sending needy and disadvantaged children first into the home counties. Of course children can be cherished in mixed-race placements, but why send the children first, when there are no black teachers, nurses or indeed few black adults to stand as role models?'

'Then recruit the black teachers, nurses and social workers!' brusquely riposted the platform speaker, a woman MP. Over coffee, several British Asian doctors from Kent approached and thanked me, saying how they also worried about the fostered, ethnic minority children whom they saw, and how strongly they agreed with my remarks.

Of course ethnic minority adults think twice before removing themselves and their families from cities, where they can share customs, food, culture, religion, values and support within their own cultural group. First-generation migrants gain succour from their certain identity – as did my penniless great-grandfather. On his arrival in Leeds, he had turned first to the synagogue. Even as third generation, my mother chose to live in a cosmopolitan part of London where many others shared her values, her political and cultural experiences. Subsequent generations, who have been educated and trained in an integrated society, evidently have different perspectives. In the '80s, we did begin to see the arrival of black health visitors, teachers and social workers in our rural towns. The commercial and restaurant sectors in rural Sussex were also drawing ethnic minority families. Today there is hardly a sizeable village that does not boast an Indian restaurant. However,

I will not forget the policy that allowed the first to come to be the vulnerable children. To my mind, these placements reflected the refusal to acknowledge either the unconscious racial attitudes or the blatantly overt racism which challenged the children.

Apart from mixed-race placements of children born in Britain, recent times have seen an increase in adoption of children from overseas. These children face change in language, new names, change from group living and sleeping to the experience of the home with a locked front door and a separate bedroom for the child. At the end of the '80s, the political collapse across eastern Europe gave rise to the inter-country adoption of Romanian orphans. The TV images of the suffering in the children's institutions were horrendous. One of the young health visitors from our clinic collected nursing materials and travelled out to work in the orphanages during her holidays. We listened to her disturbing first-hand accounts. The following autumn, I took up a one-year secondment at the Department of Health. One of my duties was to scrutinise the health forms of children under consideration for inter-country adoption and those of the prospective adoptive parents. The purpose was to clarify health issues on both sides, as a way of contributing to the durability of the arrangements. The vast majority I dealt with were about Romanian children.

This work led me to ponder hard the issues behind such adoption and the changed culture of adoption over the previous thirty years. I recalled the young women I had seen in the '60s who, because of financial liability, social censure, shame and other complex reasons, had been obliged to part with their babies. It is only recently that local authorities have been given the duty to assist parents who had given up their children for adoption, to trace and find them. Today, with lone parenting so commonplace that it evades the old censure, and with effective contraception a reality, inter-country adoption has become the realistic option for many childless couples. In the '60s, I had seen graphic images all over India of a stylised man and woman with two children, on billboards, bridges, the rear of buses and cycle rickshaws, with a logo declaring: *two children are enough.* Neither such exhortation nor the male sterilisation programme produced the desired effect. Poor people argued that each new child was an extra pair of hands to work, not an extra mouth to feed. Until couples had two children surviving to adulthood, parents were unwilling to stop having babies. The Indian population continued to expand and doubled in the half-century following Independence. China, meantime, had boasted that the Communist system could provide enough food for all. A generation later, the draconian 'one child policy' was introduced. Today, in Sussex, one sees Chinese girl babies who have been adopted by local white parents.

Sussex has changed; multiculturalism has indeed extended into the home counties. Now, when I walk across the playgrounds of the primary schools, I meet black parents collecting their own children. Local colleges actively recruit students from China and other Far Eastern countries. These students now constitute a visible presence in the rural towns. It is not just Sussex which has changed. Over the past fifty years, every part of the developed world – across Europe, the Americas and Australia – has witnessed the arrival of people from many different backgrounds, who have a contribution to make to society, actually enriching the experiences of all.

In the late Victorian period, when Annie Besant was calling for freely available contraceptive advice, she was at the same time a member of the Malthusian Society. What would she think of the global billions and the movement of peoples? How would she view the need for childless couples in Britain to look further afield to populations where innumerable children suffer lack of parental care? In Rwanda, the children who were first orphaned in the terrible massacre ten years ago are now being orphaned for a second time, as their Rwandan adoptive mothers succumb to the infection of AIDS, often contracted as a result of multiple rape during the violent civil war. The British government has pledged £1.5 billion over three years and a strategy aimed at assisting young AIDS orphans. In the early '80s a devastating earthquake flattened Managua, the capital of Nicaragua. I was in the kitchen listening to the news while washing the dishes, when I was suddenly captivated by a deeply emotive voice from Nicaragua declaring, 'Our orphans are our orphans. We will care for them. They shall not leave our country.'

It is not coal, nor fertile fields, nor fishing grounds that are the main natural resource of a country. It is the children. I can only return again to the precept of the Court Report: *The rearing of the young is the fundamental issue in human society.* Surely we have a responsibility to put children's needs first – or is there really no such thing as society?

Chapter Twenty

Prevention and Health: Everybody's Business

Grandpa's stories of his childhood had led me to search for Lithuania on the map. My own schooldays in cosmopolitan north London had extended my geographical horizons. Our early married life had brought me face to face with post-war migrants from many parts of the Commonwealth. Thus it is hardly surprising that multicultural issues have featured so prominently in my perspective on the NHS. However, ethnic minority children are only a minority group. When we arrived in Sussex in the mid-70s, 4.5% of the total population of the county were from ethnic minorities and in Lewes, it was only 1%. A generation later, the ethnic majority nationally continues as a substantial one at 92%. What was happening in the mid-70s to health care for the whole child population?

In the '60s, progress had appeared to be both inevitable and unstoppable. The welfare state and the NHS were here to stay. We rejoiced in the raft of new liberalising legislation. Hanging was abolished, homosexuality and suicide were decriminalised, the irretrievable breakdown of marriage became a legal reason for divorce. We welcomed inclusive comprehensive education, the Educational Priority Areas and raising the school leaving age to sixteen. The NHS was 'modernising'; GPs were moving from single-handed practice into groups, new GP health centres and hospitals were being built. Whilst conscious of this progress, we knew there was still so much more to be done.

The National Children's Bureau continued to publish data from their National Child Development Study. The cohort children were aged eleven in 1969. The study of these children, at the end of the 'Swinging Sixties', illustrated the Court Report's finding that the minority were as disadvantaged as ever. This minority, however, was a substantial one. The NCB publication *Born to Fail* showed that more than one in three children were either in a one-parent family, or in a large family of five or more children, or in a low-income family, or had experienced bad housing. The report collated information from doctors, teachers, health visitors and midwives. I had myself examined a couple of the children. It explored the hardships and health problems that disadvantaged children faced. Their poorer educational attainments were measured. The Report ended by asking: *Do we care that so many children are born to fail?*

Despite Macmillan's famous remark that we had never had it so good, it was well known, even in the flourishing '60s, that health, welfare, education and housing all faced enormous demands which the public purse was not meeting. Initially it had been thought that the NHS would undoubtedly raise standards of health and vitality. Through preventing illness and increasing productive years, the service would soon pay for itself. However, the costs of technical advances together with increasing longevity soon put paid to that idea. In 1976, the Department of Health and Social Security produced an important discussion document called *Prevention and Health: Everybody's Business*. In the foreword signed by, among others, Barbara Castle, then Secretary of State for Social Services, we were warned that curative medicine might be subject to the law of diminishing returns. It was imperative that the preventive approach should permeate all aspects of the Health Service, already dubbed the National Sickness Service!

The document showed how social reform, with the sanitary revolution and improved housing, lay behind the early twentieth-century control of the then common, deadly, infectious diseases. It went on to map the 1976 north–south health divide and social-class health differentials, showing the increased risk of many common illnesses and accidental deaths among the unskilled. It argued that social and environmental change could again be used to limit the prevalent top killers. Looking at the risks of smoking, alcoholism and the dangers of traffic accidents (this was before seat belts were compulsory), we were told that the responsibility for ensuring good health lay with the individual. Parents were exhorted to set their children a good example of healthy living. 'Look After Yourself' became the slogan of the Health Education Council: we cynically added – because nobody else will! The NCB Report, *Born to Fail*, shows how environmental disadvantage compounds health hazards and contributes to school failure. Surely it was self-evident that individuals acting alone cannot raise their health standards? We need community development, environmental controls and investment in children and families.

Into this struggle for health promotion and community development came a real setback. In 1973 the oil-producing countries organised into an economic consortium and drastically raised the price of oil, shifting profit making from the manufacturer using cheap energy to the primary producer of that energy. Motoring suddenly became costly: what would happen to manufacturing and our industrial base? We felt the tremors, progress went on hold, funding was at risk. When Mrs Thatcher won her historic 1979 election victory, one in six British children, 1.5 million, lived in poverty.

While there are, of course, those who are born to inherited wealth, the vast majority of us seek to provide for our children through paid work. Mrs Thatcher became Prime Minister during a period of significant industrial unrest and economic crisis. From 1979, it is well known that the manipulations of the economy, the cuts in public spending and the ending of unprofitable industries led to three million people being unemployed. Families from the north of England began to arrive on my patch, as fathers moved south to find work. Their accompanying wives were often lonely in their new situation, missing the friendship and support of their extended families and communities. These newcomers worked and saved. There was a halt on new council housing building and a general push towards increase in owner-occupation with the sale of the better council properties. Our newcomers took out mortgages. But manufacturing remained in difficulty, there were more job losses, house prices fell and mortgages foreclosed. I learned a new term: negative equity, where the mortgage owed exceeded the market value of the property.

This economic instability weighed heavily on the adults. Depression and poor health were rife, marriages broke up, children were in distress. Through the '80s, the proportion of children in poverty doubled from one in six to one in three. In our special school for children with emotional and behavioural difficulties, I noted that a significant group of our junior-aged children had spent time in bed and breakfast accommodation in their pre-school years. Of course we worked to raise the self-esteem of the children, we gave the mothers space to talk about their own anxieties and experiences of ill-health. It was not change in individual behaviour that would save these families – we needed more far-reaching change than that. During this period we watched the violence of the miners' strike on television and read the writings of miners' wives who were trying to save a way of life. Two decades later, when visiting Yorkshire, I was amazed to see new, clean, industrial work units where the mines had once been. Revitalised green parkland and environmentally conserving wetlands appeared on what had been slag heaps. If work is central to well being and family health, why in an advanced society like ours could not the run-down of mining and the development of new industry be planned in tandem, avoiding years of conflict, misery and deprivation? Did no one care to plan for this?

After Mrs Thatcher took office, among the first public services to be closed down was the community development work in which my husband was engaged. Was this 'Nanny State' work? Is there no such thing as society? My husband was not, of course, alone in being affected by these cut-backs. During this period, as the public service departments were slimmed down, those who retained their appointments worked longer hours and lost the available time to attend our voluntary evening meetings. My husband moved into the charity sector and spent the next decade or so seeking funds to build up and manage a series of projects. One of his earliest was to look at the housing needs of elderly people of ethnic minority background. He travelled around the country gathering data. When he came back from Liverpool he looked really upset.

'Can you believe it?' he asked me. 'More people begged from me during that stay in Liverpool than had I been in Kolkata.'

We were soon to experience this ourselves in Brighton and on London visits. Again I was to ask myself, how can I bear to make eye contact with a young woman with her toddler as she begs from me; how can I look away?

At the height of the rising unemployment, my husband was working for an association to support the disabled. Knowing how damning unemployment is, he proposed and applied for a grant for an exciting scheme. As disabled people often have difficulty maintaining their homes, why not get funding for unemployed skilled carpenters, electricians, plumbers to do work for them? These specialists could also employ inexperienced young people as apprenticed trainees. Funding this scheme would thus benefit three groups of people. Funding was won for a three-year period; advertisements were sent out. The piles of letters from unemployed skilled applicants were sobering. I remember him phoning one of the men to offer employment. The wife answered the phone and cried quite openly when she knew of this opportunity.

In our schools, we were increasingly conscious of the economic squeeze. Repairs were not made. By the end of the '80s I read that a third of schools in England had leaking roofs. A poor environment feeds disrespect. Both our teenagers cycled the two miles to school every day, whatever the weather. The school could not guarantee the security of the bike stands. Bike lamps had to be unscrewed every day and left in school lockers to avoid theft. Before riding home, our kids had to check the bike's mechanism. Our daughter had had a bad fall when her bike had been tampered with during the day. School could offer no redress to this dangerous, antisocial behaviour.

At a parents' evening we were told that the school meals were to be reorganised and turned into a 'Casheteria' service. When asked what supervision would be provided over how the children would select their food, the head-teacher replied, 'If your children want three plates of chips, they will be served three plates of chips. There will be no service at all if the cash tills are empty at the end of the week.'

Previously the School Meals Service had been required to supply one-third of the child's daily nutritional need. Today, we berate the obesity epidemic among schoolchildren. Meantime, it takes a celebrity cook to speak out about the lines of children queuing for burgers, chicken nuggets and chips, washed down with fizzy syrup drinks. Although twenty years too late, healthy options with fresh fruit are being introduced and improvements are promised. We need a whole cultural change towards our attitude to eating.

Continuing friction with the government led even strongly motivated teachers to join the teacher's strike. Our son had just joined his secondary school and had excitedly signed up for a parade of clubs and sports activities. Not only were these cancelled but, during the strike, teachers withdrew from lunch-hour supervision. The children were let loose on the town. When it rained, they would buy platform tickets to shelter under cover on the railway platforms.

The cut-back in the purchase of school books was scandalous. When my daughter was doing the Nuffield Biology course, there was a shortage of textbooks. Years ago I had agreed to have a photo of myself taken breast feeding our son for the Nuffield text. I never wanted such photos for my personal albums, but I had been approached by my friend who worked for BBC Schools Education and had agreed to help with this one. I hunted out the free copy of the book I had been given. Old as it was, it was more recent than the text used in her class! One of my deepest moments of angry despair was after the terrible 1987 hurricane. Making my way to the medical room in our Catholic primary school, I passed the library. The nuns in their black dresses were heaving cabinets around trying to rescue what books they could from the rain-drenched shelves. It seemed such a cruel image.

In the run-up to Mrs Thatcher's third general election, I attended an all-party meeting on education at our comprehensive school. My kids had begged me not to say anything. I sat on my hands and listened to the remarks from the platform, getting angrier and angrier. Finally I could hold back no longer and exploded at the passivity to all the cut-backs, itemising the prevalent shortages that were stopping children's progress. Where was the public rage? Why was it that in one of the richest counties in the country, the school hall was so cold that my daughter had to knit fingerless gloves to wear when writing her school exams, otherwise she could not comfortably hold her pen? I was surprised at the warmth of response from other parents and, in particular, from the teachers!

Yet what was our anger and our experience compared to what was happening in the north? In the late '70s, the Macmillan Press had brought out their Crisis Point series, debating the urgent issues facing public services. I read Paul Corrigan's book *Schooling the Smash Street Kids* which explored the responses and feelings of disaffection among youths in Sunderland. Truanting rates were high, for the boys saw only poorly paid, repetitive dead-end jobs as their future. Ten years later, Dr Hoghughi, an educational psychologist from the north-east, told of the impact of inter-generational unemployment; families where neither the fathers nor the grown children had any prospect of work. He talked about the loss of the work ethic, a culture of not expecting to work and a 'palpable hopelessness' among the young.

The three major causes of child poverty at the end of the '80s were being in a lone-parent household, or in a family with an unemployed head of household, or being the child of the working poor – employed parents on below living-cost wages. Within the NHS, the contracting out of laundering, catering and cleaning to a more cost-efficient workforce, had forced down the wages of our ancillary workers. Women fought back for a fair deal for cleaners, the Trades Union Congress ran their Day of Action and there was a massive lobby against contracting out. However, wages were forced down, cleaning posts were lost and again we later reap the whirlwind with today's rising incidence of antibiotic-resistant hospital infections. Conscious of the effects of low wages on health, I was later most gratified when in the mid-90s, our NHS Trust introduced a minimum wage before the Labour government legislated for this, and at a higher level than the wage the government eventually introduced.

Over the past ten years, the pendulum has swung again. Unemployment is currently at its lowest level for twenty years. As in the immediate post-war period, we are once more recruiting workers from overseas – especially NHS staff. Projects are under way to encourage women to train in jobs that traditionally were done by men. Fiscal measures at the end of the '90s took more than one million children out of poverty but, according to the Child Poverty Action Group, left a further three million affected by 'multiple deprivations'. We may be clever at doing heart transplants, hip replacements and treating successfully conditions that used to be fatal. Can we construct a society in which not only is every child wanted by their parents, but where every young person finds a place to contribute within society: a place which offers a sense of self-worth and lays the economic basis for the founding of a new family?

Chapter Twenty-One

Protest and Survive

Into our troubled world of public service cut-backs, job insecurity and families in crisis, came a new challenge: Thatcher's decision to buy the US Trident nuclear submarine. This led to the exhortation by the government to *Protect and Survive* – the civil defence plan in the event of a nuclear war. The nuclear threat had never gone away, but atmospheric tests had been banned. The strategic arms limitation and non-proliferation treaties had been agreed. Nuclear war itself had been dubbed MAD – the cynical acronym for Mutually Assured Destruction. Following the Cuba stand-off, we knew that a nuclear exchange would be the end for us all.

In the late '70s, the microchip had changed that fearful balance of terror. By introducing the possibility of accurate targeting of hardened bunkers and silos, we had returned to the Pearl Harbor mentality – destroy your enemy before he attacks you. War planning embraced the pre-emptive strike which contained a new form of brinkmanship. How many enemy missiles could you eliminate, how many might actually get through? We learned a new term: *the theatre of war*, meaning in effect, war contained in continental Europe. Plans were drawn up to evacuate American servicemen from the continent to decontamination units in Britain. The American Admiral G. Le Rocque said, 'We fought World War One in Europe, we fought World War Two in Europe and if you dummies let us, we will fight World War Three in Europe.'

The year was 1980. While on a family visit to my sister in Shropshire, we went to hear a GP speak about the newly formed Medical Campaign Against Nuclear Weapons (MCANW). The speaker was a woman doctor who had been on duty during the IRA bomb attack on the Birmingham pub. After completing their immediate medical care of the victims, the exhausted medical team sat together in the canteen. One of the doctors had mused, 'What if that had been a nuclear weapon?' Their talking led to the setting up of MCANW.

This question triggered an old medical student memory of mine. An elderly man had been brought into Casualty with 80% burns from an accidental fire from the then widely used, moveable oil heaters. We too had used them to heat our digs. Our patient was alive but had a terrifyingly wild look in his eyes and my fellow students were quiet and shaken.

'Have you no imagination?' I had railed at our canteen break. 'You all laughed at me for having marched to Aldermaston and now *one* severely burned and suffering man has disturbed you!'

Yes, our response to *Protect and Survive* demanded a great feat of imagination, 'to think the unthinkable, to immerse oneself in the unreal.'

I made enquiries and found that a local MCANW group was being formed – a meeting was due in Lewes the following week. I went along and met a handful of doctors, two nurses, a sister-tutor, a psychiatrist and dear old Reg. When I had first arrived in Sussex, I had gone to Brighton to a meeting to set up a local branch of the Socialist Medical Association. Mum was staying with us and, as was her wont, she came along with me. Looking across the room, she had exclaimed, 'Oh look, there's Reg!' Dr Reg Saxton had known both my parents through the SMA's struggle to plan the NHS back in the 1930s. He had been on the medical tour of the Soviet Union, to Tashkent, with my father in the 1950s. Reg had served with the Medical Unit of the International Brigade in the Spanish Civil War. There he had pioneered mobile blood transfusion, knowing speedy help could

130

save the lives of the wounded. It also led him to spend the rest of his long life campaigning against war. Frail and in his nineties, he was on the streets collecting signatures against the 2003 Iraq war. At our first encounter, Reg was a young, vigorous seventy-year-old retired Brighton GP. At the inaugural Sussex MCANW meeting, he was as animated and committed as ever.

I joined the small audience at our local Friends Meeting House. Two doctors, both GPs, were up on the platform, explaining that we all had to train and be accurately informed to answer factual questions from members of the public. They invited us to ask difficult questions to test their agility in reply.

'Two thirds of Italian cities were wiped out in the Black Death and yet these very cities revived and became the centre of the flourishing of the arts in the ensuing Renaissance. We don't want to be over-run by the Russians. Of course we must protect and survive.'

'Oh Sonya,' riposted the speaker, 'thank heavens you are on our side!'

Of course I was with the campaign. Raymond Briggs' cartoon character in *When the Wind Blows* may have used the four-minute warning to bring in her washing so that it would not be dirtied by radioactive fallout, but we already knew the catalogue of death, damage and later genetic destruction that such fallout would bring. More than twenty years earlier, on those Aldermaston marches, we had chanted, *Ashes to ashes and dust to dust – if the bomb don't get you, the fallout must!*

In 1980, the government's 'Square Leg' Home Defence Exercise estimated some 10 million deaths after a 205-megaton attack. Critics suggested a toll nearer 26 million. The British Medical Association held its own study and told us that no other country had so many people, and so many potential targets, concentrated into so small a land mass. Without Cruise missiles here, we could expect a 200-megaton attack: with them, we could expect 600 megatons. The entire resources of the NHS could not cope with the casualties of a single one-megaton weapon exploded over an urban area. The most survivors could hope for would be primitive first aid from a fellow survivor.

However, the local authority's civil defence plan found many who were willing to cooperate. We seemed to be surrounded by a sense of denial. The plan was debated at our village hall. A university science doctorate, who lived in our village, presented his calculations. His diagram showed how the steep slope of the lovely Downs would shelter our village from the blinding flash from a direct hit on Shoreham power station. He wanted stores and supplies to be prepared in the village. It was proposed that a troop of village vigilantes should be identified and kept on alert. Armed with stout sticks they would stand at the road entrances to either end of the village to keep out our neighbours from Lewes in the event of an attack. The meeting made headlines in the local press: *Men Armed with Stout Sticks to keep out Marauders.*

The BMA study was a well-documented report requiring careful reading. The wonderfully illustrated, glossy publication *The Medical Casebook*, produced by MCANW, made the issues abundantly clear. We formed a team of speakers. Reg had been active in Civil Defence for Brighton in the last war. He undertook the onerous task of reading the County Council civil defence plan and preparing a critique. I worked on the immediate and long-term effects on children, including genetic effects. Together with our sister-tutor and another GP, the four of us went to brief our MP. We each spoke for two minutes on the topic we had studied. Our MP thanked us for this material, but asserted that like the Boy Scouts, we had to Be Prepared. Once again we made the local headlines: *MP warns we must Be Prepared.*

Over the next decade our small team of some ten primed speakers addressed meetings, brains trusts, and film shows from Chichester to Hastings. We spoke to staff at the Children's Hospital and at the post-graduate medical centre and included the BMA study in the courses for student nurses and trainee GPs. At our peak we had 120 health professionals, including four professors, signed up and were the sixth largest branch in the country. We were able to commission our beautiful silk banner from a Welsh women's cooperative. We carried it locally, on London demonstrations and at the bases. It was really large and took six of us to carry it. Reg, ever the improviser, made the carrying poles from plastic plumbing pipes with ingenious holes for screws and wingnuts to assemble and steady the frame. The poles were carried in Boy Scout holsters. Reg himself usually marched carrying one of the poles. Our banner showed a blue sky over the white cliffs of the Seven Sisters. We attracted much camera attention, especially on the London marches.

There was already a strong national protest movement and, of course, the Women's Camp at Greenham Common had been set up in 1981, attracting much publicity. The anti-nuclear group was strong in Lewes. For the local CND, my husband and I prepared a programme of poetry and song on the theme of war and peace. That too stirred imagination and raised funds. The Lewes CND group prepared a theatrical programme contesting the nuclear threat. Our MCANW group contributed readings, using poetry interspersed with official statistics, which cut coldly across the poetic mood.

I well remember our large MCANW meeting in Lewes just after the BMA study was published. Our four medical speakers each gave a measured report on their brief. We covered blast, radiation, genetic, immediate and long-term effects, psychological impact, with Reg of course on the civil defence plan.

I was chair. It was a packed and animated meeting. Towards the close, Rev. Clifford Pickford, a retired eighty-six-year-old vicar, stood up and calmly railed at the sheer insanity of what he had been listening to that evening, asking whether we had all gone mad? I was thrilled. As chair, I had been attentively drawing in and briefly pointing up the contributions from the floor and was pondering how to end on an affirmative note. The vicar's contribution was unbeatable.

Although the risks of a pre-emptive strike did seem sheer lunacy to us, there remained a wider unknowing public to reach.

133

In the '50s my mother had, with great effect, used the voices of direct experience. I read in our London MCANW newsletter that Setsuko Thurlow, a Hiroshima survivor, was coming to give lectures across Britain on a ten-day tour. We asked for a visit. We entertained Setsuko in our farmhouse home. It was heart-warming to meet her. She was so brave, determined and rich with humour and love of life. She told our packed Brighton meeting how, at the age of thirteen, she had been rescued from the rubble and, with a girl friend, had joined the straggling swathes of people dragging themselves away from the city. Many were burned with weeping, open wounds and hanging flesh and were parched with thirst. Setsuko took off her blouse, soaked it in the river and squeezed drops of water over the lips of the injured. Yes, the BMA study had said the most you could hope for was primitive first aid from a fellow survivor. A press reporter asked Setsuko whether she still had nightmares.

'About that – no,' she slowly replied. 'About what is happening now – all the time. That Hiroshima bomb was peanuts compared with what we have now!'

Apart from the horror of what we risked in a pre-emptive strike, there was also the fantastic cost of the missiles. The BMA study had carefully stated that it was a scientific evaluation of the outcome of a nuclear exchange and not a commentary on policy. The following year the debate at the BMA conference extended to the immorality of the cost of nuclear weapons while people in the developing world suffered a lack of basic services. A year later the under-funding and NHS cuts at home led to a BMA conference resolution for a change in government spending. MCANW took up the slogan: *Treatment not Trident – for the cost of one Trident we could have a decent NHS*. Later we angrily pointed out that we had four Trident submarines, but what had happened to the NHS?

On our family visit to India in 1987, I contacted the Kolkata section of Indian Physicians for the Prevention of Nuclear War. The secretary, Dr Asit Ghosh, invited me to address a meeting.

134

Over fifty physicians and surgeons came and I was greeted with a huge bouquet of flowers. I spoke about how it felt to be living in a country which hosted these mobile Cruise missiles, about the civil defence plan and the cost. One medical member of the audience had recently attended an international conference. There he had been horrified to learn that one hour's expenditure on nuclear weapons could immunise all children against the five great scourges: diphtheria, whooping cough, tetanus, polio and measles. He could only describe the arms race as a sheer obscenity.

The International Physicians for the Prevention of Nuclear War (IPPNW) had been established through a joint initiative of two cardiologists, Professor Bernard Lown from the USA and Professor Yevgeny Chazov from the Soviet Union. The organisation grew rapidly with groups in over fifty countries and 140,000 medical members. In 1985 the organisation was awarded the Nobel Peace Prize for its 'considerable service to mankind by spreading authoritative information' on the effects of nuclear war. The following year saw the disaster at Chernobyl nuclear power station. Following this accident, 5000 nurses and physicians were mobilised and worked flat out, sleeping only three hours in twenty-four. They were helpless to save the thirty firemen and power workers who were at the front extinguishing the fire. The Soviet doctors sent IPPNW a message, saying that their experience at Chernobyl should arouse in physicians a sense of the great responsibility we carried for telling what is happening in the world.

We in Sussex worked hard to link with doctors world-wide. Our school nurse member represented us at the Moscow conference. Dear Reg, when nearly eighty, travelled to Japan to represent us at the Hiroshima meeting. In 1991, Reg joined my husband and myself and a physiotherapist friend at the Stockholm conference. On our return he spoke of 'a feeling of horror at the catalogue of damage already done to our planet; a feeling of anguish at the testimony of a down-winder from Utah, USA cataloguing the malignancies in friends and relatives, including the death of her own six-year-old daughter from leukaemia; a feeling of

135

indignation when the Mayor of Hiroshima recounted the disasters still ravaging his people.'

Throughout that dangerous decade only a tiny proportion of British health professionals joined MCANW, probably less than 4%, and only a handful of us spoke out in public and actively campaigned. With the collapse of communism in eastern Europe and the Soviet Union, fear of the east–west confrontation melted away. The War on Terror was soon to take centre stage. The underlying issues of poverty and health disparity remain. MCANW reformed as Medical Action for Global Security, campaigning for nuclear disarmament, sustainable development and a safe and healthy environment for all. The work continues using dialogue to resolve conflict, networking internationally and using the expertise of health professionals to raise a voice on issues of international Public Health. Yet these obviously rational objectives still appear as far distant aspirations.

Chapter Twenty-Two

The Emptying Nest

1979 was indeed an auspicious year, for not only did the British elect their first woman prime minister, but my father-in-law retired. That summer, my parents-in-law came to spend three months with us in the farmhouse. The children had the chance to enjoy their grandparents in their own environment. This included after-school outings to local beauty spots, manors and castles and, naturally, cream teas. My father-in-law knew and greatly admired English poetry. He loved our English countryside and the sight of the golden brown, Jersey cows in the fields behind our home. He marvelled at the leafy country roads, with the dappled sunlight breaking through. He loved our great trees and enjoyed his daily, independent walk over the hilltop footpath from our village into Lewes. Ma soon felt at home, cooking goodies for the children and their friends when they came in from school. My mother came down from London for a ten-day visit so she could meet my in-laws in an unhurried environment. My father-in-law stared at my mother, quietly saying, 'But I know you, and that is not just from photographs.'

We were puzzled by his clear certainty and mused over the possibilities, until we came upon this simple explanation. When my husband's family had been stationed in London in the 1950s, they had lived in the same district as us but about a mile away at the other end of the main shopping street. Most evenings, my parents would walk down to the library at that further end. We had a dog and my mother would sit on the seat outside the library with this shaggy mongrel (called Panda), while Dad went inside to read through the display of the daily papers. Meantime, my father-in-law would approach the library from his end of the main street, walk past the woman sitting with her dog and, on entering the library, he would perhaps have brushed elbows with my Dad as he too had the daily habit of scanning the press. Though they never knew each other, it was a strange sensation to think they may well have stood side by side scrutinising the library display!

That was a very happy summer for us. The following winter my mother's poor health deteriorated further and by the next autumn she was relieved of her suffering. As I sat with her in her last days, I thought much about her lost chances – her disrupted schooling, her time at secretarial college instead of university. Then I thought of her certain knowledge of what was happening in Nazi Europe. Just before war broke out, she had been able to offer refuge to a young Viennese Jewish woman and her mother, who could only leave if they had an offer of domestic employment. I thought too of how we were born in the war, of her stance against nuclear weapons, her early widowhood before she was fifty, and then her indifferent health and physical limitations. I held her hand. Looking at me, she said, 'Don't grieve for me Sonya. I have had a wonderful life.'

I returned to Sussex, for the next day my daughter was to start at her comprehensive school. As I was standing at the school gate waiting to greet my daughter at the end of her first day, my mother passed away. It happened to be the same date as her mother, my lovely Granny, had died. I am not superstitious, but I felt that that moment threaded our four generations closely together.

During our children's teenage years I was working just short of full-time and was also preoccupied with the MCANW campaign. I felt I should be doing more professionally but was uncertain how to seize the initiative beyond my existing contract. In any case, I wanted to be around for my teenagers. I knew I would have plenty of time after they had left home and I knew how fast their teenage years would pass. Both of them were already very busy with their own interests, clubs and friends.

After her O-level exams, our daughter was timetabled for two weeks' work experience. The teachers, still embroiled in their ban on extra-curricular activities, sent a letter to us parents: we knew our children, we had the local connections, we should arrange their work experience. Thus, our daughter spent a week in the specialist language unit in a local primary school and her second week in the school for children with learning difficulties. Little did I guess that she would make her career as a dedicated speech and language therapist, working on the communication and life skills of children with Down's syndrome. Watching a video of her work reminded me how hesitantly we had received little Virginia into our village school some twenty years earlier. Language therapists now start with the babies and aim to enable the children to enjoy their local primary school. As a little girl, our daughter had cried at the story of *The Ugly Duckling*. She was so distressed by the little grey creature's exclusion. Now she had her own brood to train and encourage.

Those teenage years did speed by. I kept asking myself: was this our last family holiday? After our daughter's A-levels we all went to India despite the summer heat. We must have been among the last tourists to have enjoyed a trip up to Kashmir, before the area became unsafe to visit. We returned home together with my widowed mother-in-law, just in time for the A-level results. Our daughter went off to the north of England to study. One day, while watching my husband climb the ladder for the never-ending repairs on the farmhouse, Ma scolded me.

'Why do you stay in this large rambling place? Your mother is gone. Your children will soon both be away. I shall not come any more. Move to a smaller house which you can manage!'

I was already suffering acutely from empty nest syndrome. My greatest joy had been our own children in our own home, with the regular visits of family and London friends. What did the future hold? After Ma left, the terrible hurricane of 1987 came roaring through our county. I woke at night and felt the bed shaking: the house was shaking. Looking out of the window, the trees at the front seemed to be bent double. Was this the blast from an explosion at a French nuclear power station across the channel? We paced up and down listening to the roaring sound of the wind and the sickening sound of tiles tumbling and falling off the roof. We were accustomed to the sound of the odd tile or two falling, but this seemed to go on all night. Was this the Furies punishing me for not having listened to Ma's advice? In the morning light we saw that about one third of the roof was missing. We phoned our builder. 'That's nothing,' he said, 'our roofer has lost his entire roof!' The garden was littered with broken tiles, the tall chimney had a long crack, our great sycamore had crashed across the front lawn just missing the house. Above the noise of the storm, we had not heard it fall. Yes, the Furies were telling me something: it was time for change.

For several years my husband had been on stand-by should the children fall ill. With my clinic appointments, I could not cancel at short notice, but he could work from home. Now that they were independent teenagers, he started looking at London jobs and soon took up a senior post there. We needed to move near to Lewes station so that he could readily commute. After a difficult search to find a house for which I could tear myself away from the hills and surrounding farm, we had the usual breath-holding experience of selling and buying. In those early months the farmhouse was under scaffolding, as the roof was being repaired and the tall chimney rebuilt. Many people came to view and marvelled at the oak-beamed ceilings, inglenook fireplace and the secret stairs in the cupboard that the children had loved. To my amazement, no one made an offer. After the scaffolding came down, the offers were soon lining up. Even so, for one scary month we were the nervous owners of two homes, supported by a bridging loan.

We finally said goodbye to that wonderful farmhouse and moved into a terraced house near the station. Ma had been right. The house and small garden were so much easier to manage. Weeding the borders at the farmhouse garden had been like painting the Forth Bridge. Soon the new small borders were full of flowers and our outlook was towards the same part of the Downs that we loved so much. On being taken to this new home, our cat, Caractacus (or Cracky Puss) vanished over the back wall within seconds. 'Let him choose,' said our daughter. Some five hours later we heard his familiar miaow: he had chosen to stay with us.

My husband coped very well with the travelling. Our daughter was away at university in term time and at work camps at home and abroad in the holidays. Our son had moved on to the local college. Venture scout holidays in France and Norway were far more exciting than travelling with us. They were indeed enjoying their own lives. What next? Could I join my husband on the daily commute? Should I too look for a more challenging opening in London? As usual, I regularly scanned my medical journals and newsletters on the look-out for opportunities. Then I saw it – a small paragraph saying that the Department of Health welcomed applications from practising clinicians interested in policy development, to serve a year on secondment. I phoned the number and was passed on to the Children's Division. Fortuitously, there happened to be a vacancy. Interviews to assess my suitability were followed by lengthy negotiations with my local employer. After several months, the arrangements for my year on full-time secondment were in place. I went to London to finalise starting details with my new boss.

'Well, that is all settled then. All we need do now is your political clearance.'

I said nothing, but must have turned a deathly white.

'Whatever is the matter?' my prospective boss enquired.

With lowered head, I tremulously mumbled, 'Actually, I am a member of the Medical Campaign Against Nuclear Weapons. It is a question of conscience.'

He laughingly replied, 'You could be an active member of the Labour Party but it would not debar you from this secondment.'

So I started my commuting year. I was just approaching my fiftieth birthday.

Chapter Twenty-Three

Yes, Health Minister:
Inside the Department of Health, 1990

Why was I so keen to go to London? I had been reading about the introduction of market forces into the NHS, and was totally mystified. I was working in a service which faced year on year cut-backs, after under-funding for decades. How could market forces enhance our work? Certainly the cost of care and the benefit of treatment could be evaluated for acute short-term interventions. For community services, how do you estimate the costs of multidisciplinary teamwork and where would competition come from?

It was already hard enough to fill vacancies. Even when you could get the educational psychologist to join with teachers and school doctors to evaluate and plan support for failing children, there were long queues for the therapists – who themselves could only offer time-limited strategies. Moreover, outcomes of our community interventions are measured over years. Given the dearth of professionals and the nature of our work, how could the 'market' influence us?

Most of us experienced community doctors were women who had come up through Public Health work, which had offered part-time posts when hospital paediatrics would not. We had the archaic title of Senior Clinical Medical Officer, and were viewed as 'sub-consultant'. Why should a title matter? Even before 'market forces' appeared on the agenda, the battle lines were drawn. When my own children reached their teens, I had applied to increase my work from four days per week to full-time. I was told there was no money. We were managed by the hospital paediatricians – we competed over funds. With my archaic title and perceived lower rank, I had less clout than my consultant hospital chums. My hospital paediatrician had bluntly stated, 'Look here Sonya, if it is a choice between my baby unit or your school health service, you know which will have to go!'

Thus, I had a list of pressing questions. I wanted to understand how the internal market in the NHS would affect community work. What was meant by the division into purchasers and providers? What was being planned for the health care of under-fives and schoolchildren? How would we protect staff posts and when would we get the re-grade to consultant community paediatric posts? What were the policies on nursery education, mixed-race placements, child sexual abuse? What plans were there to raise the health of the increasing number of families in poverty, the homeless families, and the children in care?

Arriving at the Department of Health, I entered my new office on the tenth floor with a staggering view across to Tower Bridge. I had a large desk with 'in', 'out' and 'pending' trays, a series of cabinets and files with intriguing titles and a note of guidance from my predecessor, who had vacated the post some months before. The office was cold and dirty with unsightly markings on the wall. I brought in cleaner and cloth, pictures and Blu Tack and stuck up images of trees, hills and water. I put up the goodwill card from one group of health visitors with the message 'We hope they deserve you!'. A second group inscribed their card 'Will think of you up there fighting the good cause!'. One primary school head-teacher had given me a big card saying 'Thank You for being a Great School Doctor!'. It was signed by all 250 children, so I would remember them and come back. My new secretary found me sitting at the desk writing with my gloves on (like my daughter doing her mock A-levels).

A couple of days later, an electric fan heater appeared. I was in my element!

There was so much to do. Each day started with the 'battle of the in tray'. I would excitedly rummage through the newly arrived pile of papers: policy documents, research papers, minutes of meetings, memos needing urgent responses. All this, plus so much in those filing cabinets that I wanted to read. Luckily I had at least ten hours' train travel each week offering guaranteed uninterrupted reading space! My husband and I travelled up together each morning, but we rarely had the chance to meet up on the return journey. As he was also working in the health arena, we were once more reading the same reports and meeting with the same colleagues on our various committees.

Taking the cue from my predecessor, I made appointments to meet those key civil servants she mentioned in her letter. I had the feeling that they were listening avidly to my expressions about the real world out there, while I was fervently lapping up titles of key reports and ongoing policy projects to which they referred. These were not small items, but drafts of major reviews of our child health services. Yes, they knew of our crisis – clinics closing, posts lost, management threatening to curtail or close down the School Health Service. But the major preoccupation was the preparation of the Guidance to the Children Act. Passed with all-party support, this Act had received Royal Assent the week after I joined the Department. In the Introduction, I found a new principle which could underwrite and protect our work. For there I read about the 'paramouncy principle': when applying the law about caring for, bringing up and protecting children, the child's welfare is paramount.

There was so much to catch up on in those early weeks that I decided to skip the canteen break with the expected chatter. Around 11.00 a.m. each day, I would hear the tinkle of a hand bell which meant the refreshment trolley had arrived on our tenth floor. I would nip out and buy sandwiches, delicious fruit yoghurt and a carton of milk, then happily retire to my desk, knowing

I was set up for the day. Soon Christmas approached and social gatherings could not be entirely ignored. Glass in hand, I was approached by a fellow doctor.

'Only been here a few weeks?' he asked. 'How does this feel after real work? Oh, don't look startled. We know, we've all been out there too.'

Members of my own section had already counselled me to slow down to avoid burnout.

Then, drink in hand, I was approached by a doctor from my section who kindly asked how I was managing.

'Oh!' I cheerily replied, 'I think I am winning the battle of the in tray.'

He looked at me reproachfully. 'But any fool can do that within the hour. We don't pay you just to do that. You should get out there and find out what others are thinking and doing about the services.'

Right! As well as teaching me to begin at the top and work downwards, Dad always said start with what you know and work outwards. Yes, my old patch – off to Camden Town, the patch I knew so well. The senior GPs I had known were still in the Group Practice Health Centre – one of the first to be set up when most GPs were still single-handed. I also checked out the name of the lead doctor for Child Protection, contacted the health visitors, and arranged to see a full day playgroup – what did that offer, how did it differ from part-time?

Everywhere I went staff were buzzing with ideas. The GPs greeted me cordially – the senior partners remembered me well and we had an animated discussion. This was the time when Child Health Assessments were being transferred from our child health clinics to the GP practices with payments to the GPs for the work. It was widely stated that the health visitors would check the children and the GPs would collect the cash. Our clinic nurses had taken over immunisations in the 1960s and, for the past twenty years, our health visitors had been doing the three key health checks between eight months and three years.

146

We doctors were assessing the new babies, seeing the children with needs and doing the full developmental and health check before school entry.

Now, one of my great regrets was that I had never had the chance to train medical students. The professor who had helped me with my membership work, had introduced me to the local course for trainee GPs held at the university. I had been booked to give a series of eight afternoon seminars. Gaining the trainees' interest and offering a new perspective proved to be a stimulating challenge. One immediate gain was to recruit one of the doctors for our service! She joined my patch and we worked in tandem for nearly twenty years. The course feedback had confirmed my feeling that I was opening new vistas for these doctors. They wrote, 'a day to get us all thinking', 'absolutely fascinating, I've never heard community medicine presented in such an interesting and far-reaching way', 'will alter my attitude not only to medicine but to fellow man'. With the cut-backs in the '80s, my eight-week seminar course was first truncated and later reduced to a single day which left me utterly drained. On the eve of child health work being passed to the GPs (on a payment basis), even my one-day course got the chop. It was one of the few occasions when my letter of protest was published in the *British Medical Journal*!

A conference to promote this changeover to the GPs was arranged in central London. The organiser invited the Health Minister to give an opening address: my boss asked me to attend in her place. As I had had various articles and letters published about the children's services, when the organiser phoned me and learned my name, he said, 'But I thought you were some doctor, somewhere on the south coast.'

'I was,' I replied, 'but just now I am with the Department.'

'Well, we are expecting some 400 GPs at the conference.'

'Good heavens!' I exclaimed, 'So many?'

'Are you nervous of addressing such a large group?'

'Of course not,' was my riposte, 'I am amazed so many are interested.'

147

'Well, they'll be paid for the work, won't they,' he cynically replied.

Both at that conference and when I travelled more widely, doctors expressed strong negative feelings about this change. When I visited Manchester, a GP there gave me a shameful account of the conditions of children he cared for.

'Why should I check healthy children when I am preoccupied with so much child distress? I work with children who lack proper shoes, who are into criminal acts from an early age, the mugging of old women on their estates. Why should I waste my time examining healthy infants?'

On the other side, clinic doctors were reluctant to lose their responsibilities. In Oxford, a senior woman clinic doctor, who was also a GP, declared that she had never been in favour of modern feminism, but seeing the way their service was under attack, she felt enraged at the threat to proper support for young and troubled mothers. A group of senior child health doctors thanked me for a fuller discussion in our ninety-minute session than at any with their consultant paediatrician over the past eight years. The senior in Exeter said she had never discussed anything at all with hers. The passion evoked by the change among professionals was strong, yet I cannot recall any public debate.

The transfer of the work to GP practices did go ahead. I later took part in training GPs in Sussex and it was the only time I can ever recall members of the audience sleeping through my presentations. Over the next ten years the frequency and content of child health assessments were continuously refined, the work passed almost entirely to the health visitors and today it is they who are offering mainly a targeted service for parents with needs. The perennial key questions remain: are parents with needs confident of how to get help and are the children with needs reaching appropriate services?

Child Protection was certainly another lead topic that year, particularly prompted by the new legislation with the Children

Act. The Camden consultant for Child Protection was astounded to have her ideas sought by 'someone from the Department'. Both she and other London consultant community paediatricians complained that their services had already been seriously eroded, they simply lacked staff. I urged that the Department was making a real push to raise protection standards, particularly for sexually abused children. I was told it was too late, as budget cuts had already taken out too many medical posts. One doctor declared she already ran a 'one-man-band'.

In the voluntary sector and professional organisations a tremendous amount of work was going on. The NSPCC was conducting a study of all the recent Child Protection Inquiry reports on children who had been failed by the services and had died. A dossier drawing together the reasons for failure was being compiled. It made alarming reading. Studying these case reports, again I asked myself – would we have done better in our patch? I attended conferences on child sex rings, ritualised abuse and staff training, and visited a centre for the treatment of sexual offenders. My predecessor at the Department had warned in her welcome letter that child sexual abuse can dominate the work. I was indeed surprised at the extent of official activity.

The Royal Colleges were preparing guidelines for doctors on identifying child sexual abuse. I observed the deliberations and was wondering how to distinguish what is family and intimate from what requires public scrutiny. Discussing this with the woman consultant who was writing the guidelines, I talked about the sensual pleasure parents normally gain from their young children's cuddles and smells, their soft skin, from the act of breast feeding.

'Think,' I added, 'how natural it is for a mum to kiss her baby's bottom.'

My colleague looked shocked. We had been standing together, and she collapsed into a chair.

'You didn't kiss your babies' bottoms did you?'

'Of course I did.'

149

'Oh Sonya, you have shocked me. Were you kissed like that as a child?'

'Of course I was.'

'How can you remember?'

Well, of course I can't remember, but I do recall Granny pinching my cheeks between her thumb and fingers saying lovingly '*kissum tochus*'. That physical expression of grand-parental love is something I can feel in my being, not recall in my mind. When I told this story to my women friends, they made good fun of me for ages. They certainly all recalled nuzzling and kissing their young babies' behinds! It would be hard if naturally non-intrusive expression of physical pleasure in one's children were inhibited by fear of these being regarded as sexually intrusive acts.

Today there is no 'fade-out' in imaging sexual experience. The romantic gentle kiss of the silver screen of my teenage viewing is out. Explicit sexual images which are self-gratifying, deviant or frankly corrupting are acceptable for public gaze, while on home TV our culture thrives on a diet of immediate gratification, domestic and sexual violence. Grandpa had blushed at the sight of an ankle. Now, the exposure of any part of the anatomy is acceptable – the bared female midriff being all the rage whatever the body volume or however cold the weather. Given all this, the vigilant training of health visitor, doctor or social worker will never, by itself, protect children. The campaigns to oppose parental smacking, to link physical intimacy to emotional connection, to suggest to the pubescent that the sexual act can wait, all demand a cultural shift towards valuing communication before action. Only a handful of child abuse cases among 30,000 examined have raised doubts about the medical evidence. The horrendous impact of mistaken professional opinion has so tarnished child protection work that today 30% of designated medical posts for child protection are unfilled. The numbers of children on Child Protection Registers has fallen from 35,000 in the mid-90s to 26,600 in 2004. Are parents doing a better job, or are professionals reluctant to identify abuse?

What of my visits to the full-time playgroups? During my secondment year, the care of under-fives was certainly under scrutiny. The National Children's Bureau was drawing up a strategy to support the developmental progress of the very young, with a curriculum for nursery education. At the Department we were working on the legislation to accompany the Children Act, setting standards for the nursery environment. Amongst the new guidelines, I read that the thermostat controlling hand-washing water in nurseries should be set at sixty-five degrees Fahrenheit to avoid scalds. I was amazed.

'How can we legislate for such refinement when one in three schools have leaking roofs...'

'That,' my civil servant brusquely riposted, 'is a political issue! We are here to draft regulations for the provision for under-fives.'

I felt myself flush.

What was the reality? During the war, the government had rapidly erected prefab day nurseries to release mothers for factory work. With demobilisation the men returned to the factories, the nurseries were closed. My father defied this move by personally examining every child in the day nurseries in his borough and stating that each needed to be there for health and developmental reasons. His nurseries remained open. I had forgotten this story, but when Mrs Thatcher, as Minister for Education, stopped the provision of free school milk in the early 70s, familiar with the health record of every child in my Camden schools I had certified that on health grounds we should continue the supply. The local Health Committee had supported this. Mum then reminded me of Dad's action to save the day nurseries after the war.

While most of the day nurseries had been closed, nursery education in the primary schools remained in short supply. We had new half-day nursery classes after the Plowden Report, but places fell far short of need. It is only within the past five years that nursery education places for four-year-olds have become a real option. When our own children were young, I and my friends joined the playgroup movement to give our children play opportunity and companionship under school age. I spent four years on the mothers' rota and thoroughly enjoyed and learned much from the experience. By 1990 the Preschool Playgroup Association (PPA) ran 17,000 part-time playgroups. Additionally there were some 600 full-time groups. What happened there?

My contact, a PPA organiser, drove me out to the back streets of Islington. There, in the corner of the tarmac playground of a typical Victorian primary school, was an old prefab nursery. Planned as a short-term measure, it was still in use nearly half a century later. I felt a shudder of familiarity, recalling those long-ago puppet shows with Dad. Inside, was just as I had remembered: the kitchen with the great range, the large guard around the heating boilers, the little toilets separated by half walls, the rows of washbasins and of pegs, the folded metal beds and grey blankets. I watched the children play, prepare for lunch and eat, talking all the while to the women who worked there. A worker who had grown up in the country wryly commented on how strange it was that children have to play with sand and water in plastic containers. An older helper regretted how the mums were missing these early years. I asked how these buildings came to the PPA. The council had built a new nursery and planned to demolish the prefab, but the PPA was desperate for places and had stepped in and offered to run the premises. The local PPA had 180 children on their waiting list, many of whom would never get a place before school age. Although this was called a full-time playgroup, to me it had all the hallmarks of day nursery care.

While many children lacked access to modern nursery provision, a worse deprivation was the housing crisis forcing families to live in temporary accommodation. Through the Health Visitors Association, I made links with SIGH, the acronym for their Special Interest Group on Housing. I read their guidance on the protection of children in temporary accommodation, and travelled to west and to east London to learn more about their work and visit some of the families. What a great group of health visitors! We visited families whose overcrowded sleeping accommodation brought back Grandpa's stories of sharing his bed with his seven younger brothers and sisters. An obvious hazard in shared living accommodation is the risk of accidents. Both SIGH and the Child Accident Prevention Trust were writing guidelines on preventing burns, scalds, falls and other accidents – but what a challenge for mums who shared kitchens and stairways with other families. In the '60s we had had a million unfit houses still in use – the image of the '90s was depressingly familiar.

A harder challenge still was to mothers who had to care for their babies and toddlers while serving prison sentences. A Department of Health team was set up to inspect the three Mother and Baby Units in prison. Our preparation was thorough: we attended lectures, read reports and conducted interviews with others who had studied prison conditions. We drew up our protocol and questionnaire, clarifying aspects we needed to examine. Nothing, however, had prepared me for the shock of seeing heavily pregnant women on their hands and knees scrubbing the floors. We saw pregnant women cleaning corridors, bars, windows and radiators using scrubbing brushes and buckets of water, doing work that was boring, repetitive and punitive. I had a flashback to the cries of the girls in the Mother and Baby Homes of the '60s, who had had to get down on their knees to polish the fireplace fenders. Even more distressing was how the women who had given birth and moved to a better prison environment, begged us to end the barbaric practice of scrubbing the floors while heavily pregnant, which they themselves had so recently endured.

Reporting back to the Department, this was the second time I found myself in tears in front of the civil servants. There was an embarrassed silence, until the woman psychiatrist in our team suddenly spoke up supporting what I had said. After a flurry of discussion, it was agreed the Home Office would be asked to intervene and stop such degrading work in advance of our full report.

Moving to the units where the babies and toddlers stayed with their mothers, we were concerned by the lack of stimulation and play. Babies lay inert on the play-mats, toddlers were strapped in buggies and lined up in front of the television. The mood of the mothers was flat or hostile. Our walk outside was peppered with mothers saying 'no' and 'don't' to the children. No leaves, twigs or beech nuts were collected by these toddlers, I never saw anyone play clap-hands or sing. When I asked a mother about toys, she replied ironically, 'A jigsaw, what is a jigsaw?'

We were complimented by the Department on our final report which was deemed comprehensive and detailed. A programme was set up to make the essential improvements including the housing of the units and staff training in child care. Yet we already knew full well from our community work how hard it is to raise the self-esteem of mothers who are so depressed and demoralised by their situation that they lack the resilience to nurture and enjoy their children. If this was a never-ending struggle in the community setting, how much more so for women who face incarceration?

The first time I had cried at the Department was with frustration, when I heard it said at the highest level that the School Health Service was for those 2% of children with special health needs and for inner-city children who lacked access to a GP. When I dared to suggest the service had a wider remit, I was sharply interrupted and reprimanded. No one else contradicted the Minister. As we left that meeting, I grabbed my senior civil servant colleague by his elbow and angrily hissed, 'Why did you say nothing? You could have supported me. For that, you must allow me a 20-minute slot to tell you what we do!'

Chapter Twenty-Four

Yes, Health Minister: Save Our Service

I had been writing accounts of these London visits and of my travels around the country and discussing them with the relevant civil servants. Whether talking about standards of nursery care, mixed-race placements, overcrowded temporary accommodation, threats to medical staff posts, the shock was to realise that the problems were not unknown to the permanent department staff – a concerted response is harder to evoke. A doctor in my section had taken me aside and told me to watch the way I talked. In a heavy tone she warned, 'To show that you care, means you will not be taken seriously.'

What is taken seriously? When discussing research objectives, it was unclear whether the task was to respond to requests for funds or lead by encouraging research that would support policy development. At a 'Stocktaking in Child Health' meeting, I learned with dismay that this was the first general review for over a year ... a year in which the service had come under severe threat. Reporting the anguish of colleagues in the field who were unable to stop the service being dismantled, and who were reluctant to hand over child health surveillance to GPs, I was told child health should have a high profile, but we can't sort things out in a panic: confusion and difficulty were likely to prevail for some time ahead.

The common concern for us community doctors was being in limbo, outside the Public Health departments since the mid-70s but not fully incorporated within mainstream paediatrics which, understandably, gave most attention to hospital services. This at the time when the business ethic and competition were being introduced into the NHS. Trusts were being set up as service providers, producing contracts to be approved and funded by commissioners in the local Public Health Departments. Together with my civil servant colleagues, I attended meetings to explain the new mechanisms to bemused consultant paediatricians. A host of new managerial posts were being established. It happened to be the period of high unemployment when graduates were hard-put to find good jobs. One of my daughter's friends had done a clerical job with her local council to save for her studies. After her graduation, she had begged the same council to re-employ her as a clerk.

On my return to my Sussex patch, I had phoned my brother. 'Guess what?' I challenged him. 'We have got a young physics graduate to run our child health services.'

'You're lucky,' he replied. 'We have a stage designer running ours.' Being a consultant psychiatrist, perhaps that was not so inappropriate.

Once contracts were in place with the cost of discrete services defined, commissioners could then ask for efficiency savings. We were exhorted to make 3% year on year efficiency savings. When we had pared any slack to the bone – including losing posts when staff retired – we were told to make 3% effectiveness savings. Were we really running services that we did not believe to be effective? That is where audit came in and, later, the National Institute for Clinical Excellence (NICE) was established to make pronouncements on how to provide excellence in care.

For years we had been struggling to raise the profile of what we did in community child health for the under-fives and in the schools. While all these changes, introducing trusts, contracts, non-clinical managers, purchasers and providers were taking place, back at the Department, my boss called me in.

'Do you remember the Court Report and the recommendation that there should be Consultant Community Paediatricians?'

I nodded, muttering, 'Of course.'

'We have a joint working party with the British Medical Association to look at the clinical work done in the community and to look at staffing needs. I'd like you to come to our next meeting.'

This was fifteen years after I had approached Professor Court. Many of us senior doctors had been through a process of accreditation. The BMA had proposed to re-grade accredited seniors as Consultant Community Paediatricians and to introduce a support post of Associate Specialist ... a title already used in hospital work. The present discussions were about assessing the need for the new posts and a transfer mechanism. Without the consultant grading, what clout would we have in negotiating new contracts for services? It was so hard to sit in silence and listen to the deliberations. Quite to my surprise, after a prolonged period of debate, my boss turned to me, saying as I was familiar with the position in the field, would I care to comment?

What a chance to speak up for the service! My travels around the country, the meetings with many dedicated community workers, had re-affirmed my belief in the service, especially for the wider range of children with special needs: the physically disabled, those with sensory loss or learning difficulties, the abused, the emotionally disturbed, the socially deprived. Health teams needed to work with teachers, social workers and others, developing community responses.

I was listened to with encouraging interest. However, the one thing I did learn during that secondment was how slowly change is negotiated, step by step. I never saw this matter through during the secondment year. When I returned to local work, I joined several national committees and was able to continue, together with other child health colleagues, to contribute to the debate. My piece in the doctors' newsletter was dubbed *Voice from the engine room*. The editor certainly understood how I felt. It was a further five years before the first re-grades were made. Our professional organisation, The British Association for Community Child Health, drew up a document delineating the nature of the work and the number of posts required on a population basis. We presented this at a large joint meeting with the BMA in London. We estimated that nationally we were short of 200 consultants. At that time there were 200 seniors so, I argued, either the work was not being done, or it was done by these seniors, of whom 80% were women, without giving them the weight of authority they needed. However, when the mechanism for the re-grade was finally agreed between the Department and the BMA, each doctor had eight hurdles to cross, the final being the personal interview before a panel of consultant paediatricians, managers and a representative of the Royal College. Through my role on the national committees, I acted as advisor and received calls from senior doctors all over the country who were struggling with the protocol. By the end of the first year, only twenty of us had achieved consultant re-grades, two from our own team. We also achieved two associate specialist upgrades – including my recruit from the GP training course.

Through the 1990s I served as our BMA representative. We received training on how to work with the media. We were taught that all policy statements must be made within eight seconds as that is the longest time people actually listen to political remarks on TV. I had not thought of that before, but began to notice how brief TV statements were. We had fun working up slogans. I liked the one that went 'advertising corrupts, smoking kills'. However, if eight seconds was the average listening time, how should we set about defending the NHS?

I went to BMA training days to learn how to negotiate health service contracts and worked with colleagues from various disciplines and from all around the country. We practised role play; one group of doctors were the managers, I was in the clinicians' group. We each had a briefing paper on the issues to be discussed within our own group. When we went to the role-play negotiation meeting, we found the parameters had been changed by the management, unbeknown to us. Our lead consultant, a physician, was furious. He began to bang the table, then looking at the rest of us, indicated that we leave the meeting and we all walked out. Our trainer was horrified.

'You can't do that,' he declared. 'You have to negotiate around the changes the management want to introduce.'

'I will not debate differential pay based on speciality,' announced our leader. 'This is a National Service and parity of pay makes for successful recruitment across the different specialities. Anyway the arguments in there have sent my pulse racing and I'm getting heart-burn!'

He grinned at us and dramatically felt his own pulse. Behind his grin, this consultant physician was not joking. Critics called our NHS an old-fashioned, over-centralised monolith, but we knew what amazing benefits had been realised during our working lifetimes. Centralised funding and planning, together with a resource-allocation mechanism to support needy areas, meant that wherever you lived, you had twenty-four hour access to the GP service and were within reach of a District General Hospital. Moreover, national standards of training, employment and pay minimised administrative costs. We sensed that the internal market, with the competitive business ethic, would threaten the cohesive teamwork, goodwill and vocational commitment that was our culture and on which so much of the effectiveness of our work depended.

Most of the doctors at these training sessions were men, as were most of my colleagues on the professional committees and yet we child health doctors were predominantly women. While I was at the Department, the Hansard Society Report *Women at the Top* had been published. Sitting at the back of Department of Health meetings with swathes of doctors in front of me, I could see that the overwhelming majority were men and almost all were white. I met Asian staff in the clerical sections and the canteen staff were black. The Hansard Report told of the glass

159

ceiling confronting women, blocking their aspirations. Women could see where to go, but frustratingly could not get there. The Department of Health devised a series of programmes to help women through the glass ceiling inside the Health Service. On my return to Sussex, I applied for such a course and was invited to a residential weekend in one of our ancient hotels in an old village in the central part of our county.

I signed in, excited to be joining this two-day course. The other women arrived. I seemed very old, being then in my fifties, while they appeared to be at least ten years younger than myself and all so smartly turned out. I remember I was wearing my 'solidarity with the women of Guatemala' jacket made of brightly patterned patchwork pieces, but hardly the smart cut of the black power-suits my colleagues wore. Perhaps it was a bit late for me to challenge the glass ceiling! They aspired to be chief executives or to hold other high offices in health care planning. We sat around an oval table. The course leader explained that he had been a clinical psychologist in the NHS but was now with a private firm of industrial psychologists advising on career development. I grinned.

'You mean you are one of the rats that has left the sinking ship, and now you have come back to teach us poor fools how to swim!'

It was most interesting to listen to the formal presentations by the other women about their work and to debate with them the new purchaser/provider NHS. But when we were given business games to play, I felt exasperated, as I could not see their relevance. Sometimes what we had to do seemed so silly, I began to opt out. The sessions were intensive and towards the end of the course we each had a private interview with an experienced high-achieving woman who was working in NHS administration. Mine sympathetically leant towards me, saying, 'I can understand that you have served a long time in the service, you know a lot, but you should be careful to avoid openly resisting the changes. You really need to work with them.'

160

'Look,' I responded, 'my grandparents came to this country as refugees with nothing. My parents witnessed poverty and social injustice and campaigned hard for the NHS. We grew up with the NHS and my brother and I have trained and worked within it. Now our children are training in health care, but will they find a place in the NHS? And when we are old, will it be there for our needs?' Then, with TV images from the recently collapsed Soviet Union in my mind, much to my chagrin, I suddenly and tearfully burst out, 'and the children are begging in the Metro in Moscow!'

My mentor leant forward and placed her hand on my knee saying, 'Sonya, be kind to yourself.'

Around this time, my mother-in-law came over for what was to be her last trip to England. She saw her grandson courting, was taken out by them for a cream tea and told me on her return that those teenagers would marry – which indeed, years later, they did. Together with our daughter, we four set out for a brief trip to northern France as Ma had always wanted to see that country. That year I was President of the Society of Public Health and as such was invited to the congress of the sister Irish body. With Ma we travelled to Athlone. Purchasers and providers and GP-delivered children's services were not on the Irish agenda. The meeting was enjoyable, the doctors were so friendly and kind. Travelling with Ma attracted much attention, again in a courteous and kindly manner. I talked with Ma about my work and what I was up to. She scolded me terribly, reminding me what a punishing and stressful time her husband had had in administration and central government work.

'Sonya, in your clinics you see people and you can help them. Why think of doing anything else!'

No, Ma was right, I had learned that my best work was in the clinics with the parents and children who needed what we could provide – I sensed that on the prison inspection visits through my contacts with the mothers there. However, when I returned to Sussex, despite that enriching year at the Department, my old employers could still only offer the four-day contract. I was stunned. A full-time senior vacancy came up in the adjacent Trust at Brighton, I applied and transferred, and thoroughly enjoyed an exciting last decade of work with them. My vacated post was advertised as ... full-time!

Of course Ma had been right. After my skirmish with the Minister about the work of the School Health Service, I had indeed had that chat with two of my civil servant colleagues, telling them what it was like to work inside the schools. I showed them the data I had been collecting about need, and talked about our links with other services. Finally, I showed them the card signed by the 250 children in one of my schools with the head-teacher's request that I should not forget them but should go back. As I finished, the senior civil servant commented, 'Why don't all our schools have a service like that?' and then giggled his nervous defensive laugh that I had heard so often.

On my return to the field, the School Health Service was continuing to shrink and remained under attack. The British Paediatric Association had set up a working party to delineate the health needs of school-aged children. We worked hard to define the tasks that needed to be done and who should do them. The school nurses already had an enhanced role and were doing the health assessment of new entrants for whom there were no concerns. We doctors concentrated on supporting those with difficulties. The school nurses were increasing their teaching and counselling work, and many were active in family planning. I attended a seminal conference in Leeds where the evidence was debated. The final report referred back to the original work in 1904 which had led to the setting up of the School Health Service. Many of the young men who had been called up to fight in the Boer War had been in such poor health that they could not be enlisted ... 'the scandal of the rotten recruits'. The service had been introduced to deal with this 'physical deterioration' in the young population. Looking at today's problems, issues relating to poverty and disadvantage were as relevant now as then. Perhaps, the report suggested, that is what community paediatrics is about.

Which leads me to the story of 'children in need'.

Chapter Twenty-Five

Children in Need

December 1990: my elevated year on the tenth floor ended and I returned to clinical work ... a real come down to earth. At my first clinic, the very first mother I saw started to cry as my enquiries about her child revealed that she was an unrecognised agoraphobic, sending her daughter to school by taxi which she could not really afford. By the end of the morning I felt as if I had never been away. Walking into our residential school for emotionally and behaviourally disturbed children, our county psychologist gave me a big grin, saying, 'Welcome home Sonya.' It *did* feel like home. Our head-teacher reported that a ten-year-old lad had been sexually assaulted (buggered) by one of our older boys in front of his mates. A case conference was planned – new style with parents present. While the teachers and social workers led the discussion, I pondered much on all I had seen and learned during my year away.

At one of our comprehensive schools, there was an outbreak of hysterical over-breathing among fourteen-year-old girls. The school secretary felt demented at having to call an ambulance three times in one day as the girls collapsed semi-comatosed. I cancelled the clinic appointments and went over to the school. In a gruelling morning I sorted out the one true, poorly controlled asthmatic from the five emotional 'copycats'. Next, I saw each of these five girls quietly and individually to ascertain their varying reasons for feeling panicky, emotionally unsteady or depressed. Then there was a protocol to write for the school secretary and teachers on how to help the girls and when to call the ambulance. Certain of the girls needed follow-up appointments at our Family Clinic. Some attended alone, some with their mothers.

As this was winter time, I soon caught infections from the younger children I saw at clinic and nursery class. I began to feel weighed down again by pressure and fatigue. The difficult contest with my employers over my four-day contract was ongoing. By the end of the first month, I felt that I had lost all the physical benefit of that year of paperwork and debate. Then I transferred to Brighton.

Our lead doctor welcomed me with a broad smile. We had already been colleagues on neighbouring patches for fifteen years. We had met at meetings and conferences. While at the Department, I had been feeding her the information I was gleaning about service changes. Her smile faded, however, as she adopted a more serious tone, warning me with these words, 'Look here Sonya, you are welcome aboard but I steer a steady ship, and I'll not have you rocking the boat.'

What a great 'captain' she was! Quick to ascertain and develop the strengths of team members, she gave space for each of us to work up our particular interests and enthusiasms. She was the true doctor/manager – she even had that particular skill of optimising the budget. Slightly older than myself, she had trained at Cambridge when it had been a real triumph for a woman to secure a medical student place there. Given the developing ethos of the contract-driven service, she encouraged me to take on the audit of our work.

Following the thrust to promote the business ethic, during my summer at the Department we had received a cascade document asking for a Mission Statement for Child Health. Surely our mission derived from my favourite quote from the Court Report: *The rearing of the young is the fundamental issue in a human society.* I had proceeded to tease out what this meant in the business jargon of goals, priorities, aims and objectives for children's services. My paper was never discussed. At my departure six months later, I had dug it out and sent it round the team again, as my farewell cry, my valediction.

The keen interest I had brought back from the Department was how to identify children in need, as newly defined by the Children Act. We already had a register of children with special needs – the physically disabled, those with chronic intrusive illness, the learning disabled, children with marked emotional problems. These were the 2% of schoolchildren who, since the 1980s, were entitled to statutory support aimed at keeping them in mainstream school where possible and special school where necessary. The importance of the School Health Service for these children was recognised ... even at ministerial level! What of other needy children, those unlikely to achieve or maintain a reasonable standard of health without access to services? This was the group the Children Act newly defined as those 'in need'. The National Audit Office were concerned that the Social Services were concentrating so strongly on children needing protection that they were not providing for those with other needs. Our Child Health Services were cautioned that we were working so hard to provide the universal child health assessments that targeted work on those with needs was missing out.

I discussed this with the child health doctor I had recruited to our team from the GP trainee course. As nursery class places fell far short of parent request, our schools prioritised youngsters with needs, so we knew there would be clusters of children in need there. We each assessed the children in our respective nursery classes, writing profiles of those we considered 'in need'. Together, we compared our lists and presented the material at a team meeting of our dozen community child health doctors – all of us were women, several from overseas. We debated the interpretation of need and prepared guidelines for nursing staff. The medical or developmental condition did not define need, but it did underlie the assessment of need. The key message emphasised the value of the holistic assessment of the child within the context of the family.

Focusing on pre-schoolchildren aged around three years, we prepared and asked our two dozen speech therapists and eighty health visitors to identify such children in need, over a given period. At the same time, the child health doctors were also asked to prepare a list of those in need in the same age group, who were seen in the nursery classes they covered. We were all working with the same child population but from differing perspectives. I then looked for concordance between the children selected by the three groups of staff. We analysed the differences, looking for what was deemed important by the various professionals when selecting their children.

There was, as expected, high concordance in identifying children with special need, but marked variation for the children in need. This variability was discussed and hotly debated at a whole-team meeting. One of the key issues was the perceived level of acceptable health. This imagined line was moveable depending on the population served. What was not acceptable in well-off areas was tolerated where other children had far worse difficulties. Following this debate, training sessions were run to harmonise awareness of what characterised 'in need'. One particular problem which had not been given full enough importance was poor language skills influencing poor behaviour in the three-year-olds. Our speech therapists led on that training.

Case presentations of examples of children in need were given in groups of around a dozen staff to allow fuller question and discussion time. When this preliminary work was completed, a code to record 'special need' and 'in need' on our computer system was selected. We could then analyse the prevalence of children in need by postcode. In the meantime, the work was extended to the two dozen school nurses who were, at that time, still seeing all parents of five-year-old school entrants for a health interview. Thus we could get a picture of changing need from age three to five years.

The difference between inner-city and other children had already been well documented in other studies. In general, health and educational problems are twice as common among inner-city children. As expected, our work showed a concentration of children in need in our deprived inner urban areas. What we did not know was the extent of the difference. We found eight times the concentration of children in need in our struggling areas compared with the more salubrious suburban and rural districts. Moreover, in deprived areas one in four three-year-olds and school entrants were assessed as 'in need'.

The health visitors and school nurses had both expressed concern that focus on 'in need' would leave out the vulnerable children who also merited support and for whom the nurses' support was often the only help provided to the families. In my own nursery school, while 25% were 'in need', 40% of three-year-olds were selected by nurses and teachers for medical assessment. The majority of all children seen needed continuing support or investigation. We decided to log the vulnerable children as a separate category. This showed that across the Trust, vulnerable children proved to be almost as numerous as those in need. We published this work and received invitations to present the project at various conferences in London and elsewhere. Eventually our local work was used to locate and inform our Sure Start programmes.

Following this success, each school year we would select new aspects of our work to investigate. The presentations of the collated material had to inspire the team to make them feel it was worthwhile to collect the data; for this was an additional chore just at the time when staff were learning to make computer entries of their daily patient contacts. Over that decade we looked at referral pathways for under-fives with developmental delay and for three- to six-year-olds with emotional and behavioural problems. We developed guidelines to enhance appropriate referral. We assessed the support offered by school doctors and nurses to bullied children aged nine to fourteen years, registering outcomes for the children six months later. We logged the contribution to child protection case conferences; the work with children who wet and/or soiled; we evaluated health advisory contacts with adolescents; and the nature of health assessment and support given to fostered children. Each project was a time-limited snapshot, but read together, the projects illuminated the nature of child health work in the clinics and schools. The projects were used to inform our Trust managers and were also shared with our local Public Health Department commissioners. We regularly published outcomes as journal letters, articles or conference contributions. The work stimulated responses from other Trusts.

Over that decade, I found I was working harder than ever, both on our local patch and travelling to conferences and meetings around the country. When I finally got my consultant re-grade, my husband suggested that he took early retirement to stay home and look after me properly! Well, I mused, I had relished those middle years of part-time work and home with the children. Both were now adult, one in work and one spending time living with family members in India. Yes, it was time that my husband had the space to pursue his musical interests. Of course he should have his time 'at home'. Our ageing cat would certainly enjoy the company.

The Family Clinics were as busy as ever and the concerns raised by parents were constantly challenging our knowledge and awareness. As conditions like autism and hyperactivity became discussed in the media, so too parents came forward with their questions, seeking assessment. Parents of adopted children came with concerns about unusual developmental patterns; they had no family members against whom to compare such traits. Issues relating to open adoption and contact from birth mothers were raised. Letters from birth mothers were shared with me. Following work at the specialist centre for child sex abuse, families would come to us for support for adjustment problems at school after key work was completed. I met fathers who, having never been with their babies, were seeking contact after gaps of up to five years. How do you reach a balanced consideration when the child's needs must be paramount? How do you consider the wishes and feelings of very young children? The evaluation and decisions were made at the Family Court.

Families came forward where both parents were of the same sex. Had such families never been formed before or was it only in the '90s that women felt strong enough to approach the clinic as a parenting couple? A troubled mother approached, on the advice of the class teacher, for help with her ten-year-old daughter. Her opening remark was one I had heard so often, 'My husband has left me...' then, watching me closely, she added, 'for another man.' None of these issues could be resolved in the Family Clinic alone: the majority required careful team working with the schools, community nurses, educational psychologists, local social workers. The few were referred on to specialist hospital paediatric or child psychiatric services. With our focus on community support, we felt we truly knew what joined-up working meant.

After the election of the 1997 Labour government, we received a missive from the Regional Director of Public Health. There was going to be a push for 'Healthy Children'. We were all asked to prepare a list of: 'IMPORTANT POINTS FOR WHICH I WOULD DIE IN A DITCH'.

I sent the following:

- Cultural change to raise the value and importance of parenting.
- Effective fiscal support for families with children.
- Child-inclusive design of homes, shops, leisure facilities, transport.
- Value all staff who work with children (including child minders).
- Measurement of effective strategies.
- Sense of confidence in the future.

During my last years at work, the new Labour government did not move on from the old spending plans. We felt we had worked so hard against all the cut-backs to give visibility and claim value for our work in community child health. Our team was intact with consultant lead and associate specialist support. I began to hear promises of increased funding, plans for restructuring giving commissioning responsibility to the new Primary Care Trusts. We had a meeting about the introduction of Sure Start. (Hadn't we had Home Start and Educational Priority Areas in the '60s, only to see them abandoned?)

How did we feel about yet another reorganisation? The proposed new boundaries would split our Trust. Our much respected Clinical Director, who had warmly welcomed me aboard and who had been such a supportive colleague, was now retired. Was the race really run? Was it time for me also to hand over to younger doctors, to let them cope with the new organisational ideas?

The culture of medical practice is always evolving. Amongst new medical students, women are now the majority and nearly a third are from ethnic minorities. Our Medical Action for Global Security organisation has an active student section. Will the struggle to establish the NHS, and the poor health care conditions changed by the service, be remembered? Will the close link between health and disease with our living conditions, inform future service developments? Will the campaign to protect children and families be high enough on the public agenda? Will we really achieve a National Health Service not just a National Sickness one? So much remains to be done.

Chapter Twenty-Six

Children in Need in Europe – and Beyond

During my visits around the country in that secondment year of 1990, I had learned of the European Society for Social Paediatrics (ESSOP) and had joined up. Three groups of children were recognised as meriting special consideration: those with special need, with protection needs and with cultural need. With a strong input from the Scandinavians, ESSOP was debating the health-promoting society, the social changes required to support children and the role of a National Ombudsman for Children. Meantime, the political changes in eastern Europe had given rise to a burgeoning of new ideas there. Together with my husband, we travelled eastward to learn what colleagues were up to.

Our first foray was in 1993, back to Poland. The ESSOP conference was in Rabka, south of Krakow. There were no direct flights to Krakow which met with our schedule. However, I had kept in touch with one of our Warsaw friends and although we had not met for 26 years, since the late 1960s, we had exchanged the annual Christmas card.

'Of course you will stay with us. I meet you at the airport. I book your train tickets to Krakow. Will you know me? I am old man with grey hair...'

At the airport, I nervously scanned the crush of people against the barrier. Instant recognition. Ryszarda drove us in his little Fiat to the bank. I glimpsed the new McDonald's and massive, shiny office blocks of reflecting glass, threatening to diminish the towering, Soviet-built, 'Palace of Culture'. Ryszarda would not let us change as many travellers cheques as we wanted to. 'Too many zloty,' he mumbled as we gathered up the six million.

'Look at me,' he said as we clambered back into the little Fiat. 'Old man, grey hair, small car. Look at he,' as a sleek Mercedes drew alongside at a red traffic light, 'young man, black hair, big car. Something happened in this country!'

'Please come,' he gently requested and took us to a nearby church. He showed us an inscription to his eighteen-year-old brother, killed in the opening air raids of 1939, and that for his father, killed in the Warsaw uprising.

The environment: invasion, war, oppression ... still such a close, real experience. At the conference, Professor Mazlarka presented charts of industrial pollutants, maps illustrating fearfully contaminated rivers and plans to purify these within five years. At a later ESSOP conference I learned that the clean-up was actually achieved.

'We have just finished the five-year programme of giving iodine to our children because of Chernobyl. But I fear for them, I fear for their future,' spoken with sadness and dignity by a Polish woman paediatrician.

'Arms conversion or destruction of the industrial workers family!' exclaimed our new friend, a paediatrician from Katowice.

At the conference opening, children from a local village gave a breathtaking performance of *musica antiqua*, playing crumhorns and sackbutts, slipping from one piece to the next, singing, dancing and playing – with cues or conductor unseen – as they performed immaculately with modesty and total commitment. Even their leather slippers looked authentic. The children of Rabka presented their video showing how they had collected sackloads of litter and rubbish from the beautiful hills surrounding the towns. They emptied the sacks in the town centre square to shame the townspeople and to demand greater respect for the birds and animals who inhabited the hills.

This challenge reverberated through the gathering of children's doctors from across Europe. The conference theme of 'Children and the Environment' bore significance for us all. Considering the challenges of ozone layer depletion, global warming, water shortages, surely the task of securing a healthy environment today is as great – perhaps even greater – than that faced by our Victorian forebears in their unhygienic, smog-polluted, newly industrialised world.

War and armed conflict, the greatest environmental challenge of all, was only too evident at the following ESSOP conference at a kibbutz in the pine-clad hills outside Jerusalem. On our arrival, the scented evening breeze with the distant chanting of the mullah had lulled our senses. But the pervasive presence of men and women soldiers, the news of casualties from the terrorist bomb in a bus in nearby Tel Aviv and the conference subject of 'War and Children' kept us acutely aware of harsh realities.

Dr Ofra Ayalon, a distinguished psychologist from Haifa, showed a film about the life experiences of the child survivors of the attack on the holiday camp at Ma'Alot in 1974, where over twenty children were killed in a confused riot of shooting and running, while fifty children managed to escape. The subtlety of the film lay in the profound intimacy of the interviews with the now adult survivors, twenty years after the experience. The words and images both of the survivors and of their family members, the survivors' guilt, the grief for a lost sister, had a penetrating, haunting quality which related to outcomes for children caught up in violent conflict anywhere.

This conference was during the time of war in former Yugoslavia. Dr Josef Grguric from Zagreb used graphs, photographs and children's drawings to illustrate the horror of civil war where children can find mother and father – Serb and Croat – on opposing sides. He did a joint session with Dr Ayalon. She talked about the use of psychodrama and guided fantasy to enable distraught and troubled children to deal with chaos and panic.

'You cannot prevent the birds of sorrow from flying overhead; but you can prevent them from building nests in your hair.'

175

The words sounded brave, the reality challenged their value. During our brief stay, the Peace Accord was signed between Jordan and Israel. On that evening we were at a date-cultivating kibbutz at the northern end of the Dead Sea. At our communal supper, a large cake with iced decorations of the Jordanian and Israeli flags was cut. Our tables were decorated with olive branches. We toasted 'Peace', 'Shalom'. We gazed across at the pink evening light on the hot, rugged, seemingly deserted hills of Jordan. As dusk gathered, distant lights glimmered across the sea. Our hosts pointed out those of Amman. Despite that hopeful night, the ensuing decade brought nothing but grief and torment on an unthinkable scale across the Middle East.

It was in Istanbul that School Health was the conference topic. We had arrived several days beforehand to stay in central Istanbul and see something of that dramatic city with its beautiful mosques, renowned sea straits and ancient Roman remains. There had just been the terrible earthquake which had demolished 10,000 homes in a poor area east of Istanbul. Our flight was empty, the small hotel was sparsely occupied and the streets were devoid of tourists. Zig-zagging through the lanes of the old city between bazaar and mosque, through small roads humming with people and busy with donner kebab stalls, one rarely saw a woman. I felt very self-conscious. Accosted by insistent carpet sellers displaying their dazzling array of patterns and colours, I began to wonder whether all the women were locked away double-knotting warp across weave, waiting to find the cry 'Rumpelstiltskin' to set them free.

Dr Gulbin Gokay, President of the Turkish Child Health Association, and for that year President of ESSOP, must have found the magic name. She had organised an excellent conference. On leaving the head-scarved women behind in the old city, I entered the universally familiar, spacious, glassed foyer of the conference hotel. I found myself among over 150 Turkish women health professionals, smartly dressed in dark trouser suits, with their rich glossy hair of varied colours and textures flowing free around confident excited faces. The workshops buzzed with

176

animated enquiry, emphatic expression of concern and expressed gratitude for the presence of us few foreigners at the conference.

Turkey had only recently extended state education upwards from eleven to fourteen years. The School Health Service covered 20% of the total population providing primary access to health care. Classes had seventy children, teachers worked split shifts in buildings with inadequate toilet provision, funds for water and electricity ran out. Children came to school without breakfast, eating bread and sweet snacks from street stalls. This evoked images of our schools when our School Health Service was first set up in 1905, which is why we had introduced free school milk and nourishing school dinners at the outset. My mother, schooling in Edinburgh, had been one in a class of sixty children, when she had been *Dux*.

Ms Juszczak, a nurse practitioner from New York, described a similar situation among their black and Hispanic children today, for whom school-based health care was the only primary health care available. I had been dreadfully shocked by Jonathan Kozol's account of Boston schools in *Death at an Early Age*, which I had read when in my twenties. I had hastened to read his return to such schools after a thirty-year absence in 1991. Titled *Savagely Unequal*, it gave a depressing image of widening disadvantage and exclusion over the interim decades. The Turkish paediatricians argued for an inclusive school environment which values and protects the individual child. 'Everyone suffers in an unequal society.'

These gatherings always brought new images and ideas. If we thought we faced an uphill struggle in Britain, what about the fringes of Europe and beyond? In the late '50s my father had immunised us three children with the then new, injected vaccine against polio. Travelling to India a decade later, I had seen numerous children still attacked by that paralysing disease although by that time we had the oral vaccine. Nearly thirty years after I was vaccinated, my brother's son, while a medical student, took part in a polio vaccination campaign in Malawi. The slow progress was due, in part, to the difficulty in securing a 'cold chain', a method of keeping the oral vaccine stable while travelling from central to peripheral rural populations. We have been so clever in other methods of temperature control – for example the use of deep freezing to maintain fertilised eggs – why has it taken so long to deal with this problem? It is only in recent years that world-wide polio eradication has nearly been achieved. A permanent state of alert is required. Ethiopia appeared to have eliminated the disease in 2001. Following the recent diagnosis of a new case there (in 2005), a programme to further vaccinate 100 million children in twenty-two African countries is currently under way.

While we argue for better health support for needy children at home, the key issue elsewhere is the 'Roll Back Malaria, TB and AIDS' programme. TB, the White Plague, has returned with a vengeance. In Victorian times, we lost so many gifted young people to tuberculosis that the disease was dubbed the White Plague or Captain of the Men of Death. It was neither mass X-ray nor potent drugs which rolled back TB here, but better housing, improved nutrition and less congested living. I learned about this on my Public Health course, where we had befriended the fellow student from (the then) Rhodesia who was running his TB 'crusade'. The disease has remained the global Captain, the top killer. Writing about his work in the '60s, our friend had railed:

I am forced to the conclusion that however limited staff and finance may be, the major handicap is not the fact that modern medical knowledge cannot be applied, but simply that it is not applied and no serious attempt has been made to apply it consistently… It is only by mounting a Crusade that we will ever get doctors to do what sheer human compassion should have prompted long since.

Independent Rhodesia became Zimbabwe. Today in Zimbabwe, poverty, forced dispossession and under-nutrition alongside the spread of AIDS, increases the susceptibility to TB. The social basis for the spread of the White Plague advances. Throughout sub-Saharan Africa, millions of new cases are being recorded. The World Health Organisation has declared TB an emergency in the African continent. The emergence of the disease in the overcrowded, impoverished inner-city areas in New York and among the prison population in Russia further illustrate how poverty, social exclusion and lack of access to health care are the key factors in the spread of the disease. The words of our friend in the '60s are even more telling today. Despite the launch of the Roll Back Malaria campaign in 1998, only about one in seven children in Africa sleeps under a mosquito net and only 2% under insecticide-impregnated nets which offer greater protection against the malaria-carrying mosquito and could save so many children's lives.

Meantime, while companies in the west have agreed not to produce any more 'king-sized' chocolate bars, 90 million children world-wide are 'severely deprived' of food. The limited goal of providing safe drinking water to 25% of the world's population by 2015 is not being reached. While there are 15 million child orphans as the result of AIDS (a figure predicted to rise to 20 million), war, particularly civil war, remains the greatest scourge. Over 90% of armed conflicts in the last decade of the twentieth century were within, not between, countries and children numbered among half of all those killed.

When I was a child myself, sitting with my family of seven eating our meals together, I was watched over by a charming picture of three smiling boys – one African, one European and one Chinese. The logo read: *we are all one family*. Well, we have the global economy, we have the global village. Will we ever achieve that global family?

Chapter Twenty-Seven

The Millennium

In the summer of 2000, I did retire. We organised a celebration party for family and friends at the beautiful Southover Grange, owned by Lewes council, just down the road. My son produced a helium balloon with the logo *Forty Years of Magnificence*. Of course we put on our own entertainment: a series of vignettes telling the stories of the women who had made my career possible. The words of my forebears in poetry, quotation and ironic dialogue which I delivered were interspersed with music hall and parlour songs sung by my husband. When we got to the suffragettes, our whole audience joined in the chorus of the music-hall jingle of the womanising MP who supports votes for petticoats:

> Put me among the girls,
> Those with the curly curls.
> They'll enjoy themselves and so will I,
> If you put me among the girls.

Colleagues arranged their farewells in the various work settings. My own child health sector team of doctors, nurses, secretary and nurse assistant arranged an 'at-home' evening supper party where each brought a different dish. Sitting around a long oak table, eating, joking and laughing, we all had great fun. I was called upon to make a speech ... my last official one?

181

I told them that it seemed to me the past 40 years had passed in what felt like 40 minutes. I could easily remember how I had felt when, as a student, I had approached a woman patient with thyroid disease, to take blood for the first time. I can still recollect my anxious insecurity. I can recall my patient's face, in particular her smile and her encouraging words. That was the marker of the privilege we had enjoyed over the years; the gift of our NHS, this great cooperative venture. We could offer our training and knowledge to people without ever wondering whether they could pay. We opened ourselves to the concerns and worries of others. Their cooperation and trust were our constant reward. We staff come and go, but the team will carry on. I knew there would be a few ripples with my departure, but these would soon settle. We are all but a pebble in the stream.

'No you're not,' interrupted my GP-recruited colleague, 'you're a ruddy great rock!'

A shudder flitted through me, with Granny swaying and weeping in my arms at my father's death, 'My rock, my rock of Gibraltar is gone.'

Of course the work went on. Our team was broken up, new allegiances were formed. Targets and changes in working practices soon followed. I watched as children's issues moved up the national agenda. First, the start of fiscal changes to lift children out of poverty. Then the emphasis on targeted work for needy children, Sure Start programmes with new nursery and community buildings, a Minister for Children – even a programme for Africa. I also watched the introduction of public–private finance initiatives, the active recruitment of doctors and nurses from countries whose health needs were so much greater than our own, the extension of profit in health care delivery. I wondered how the founding principles of the NHS could be maintained.

All my retired women friends take on voluntary work. I chose to visit ten-year-olds in a local school, who need support with their reading. At my weekly visit, I call the children out in turn, to read and chat with me. We read at a table in the corridor, which I brighten up with my weekly bunch of flowers. Each child gets a prize – a choice of a calendar picture, fancy bookmark or colourful postcard. As I enter the school and walk down the corridor, the children are coming in from after-lunch play. They run up to me urgently calling, 'Please, please miss, can I read today?' One of the boys asked in a puzzled voice, 'Why do I like reading to you, miss?' while one of the girls approached, cheerfully saying, 'You know, miss, you really are a nice lady.' Yes, I have my own group of 'Edwards' now.

Whatever happens in children's lives, I have always believed that continuity of emotional experience derived from the home, the school, the community, is of fundamental importance. This story started with Granny's loving caress, it will close with another story, extended from those our loving Grandpa used to tell.

After my retirement, we fulfilled a long cherished dream to visit the family in Australia – those aunts who had not sent the sweets for good children to my infants' school. Grandpa's father was one of five brothers who had each fled Lithuania as they reached their eighteenth birthday. Three arrived in Scotland, met up and settled there, two raising their families in Edinburgh, one in Glasgow. Separately, the two other brothers had made the passage to Australia and lived in Sydney. By a series of chance events, the Scottish clan eventually made contact with the brothers in Australia. It was Grandpa's youngest sister who emigrated to marry her first cousin in Sydney, early in the twentieth century.

Now, on our visit, we were captivated by Sydney's beautiful harbour, edged by the wonderful botanical gardens in which ibis strutted and flying foxes hung in the trees. The family gave us a most loving welcome. We arranged to meet up to see an exhibition in the art gallery and to lunch in the restaurant there, with its stunning view over the city and harbour. As we sat around the table, talking and laughing, I thought here are my two aunts, both recognised artists, both in their mature years still exhibiting new works. Here is my Australian cousin, an art teacher. We other two women in the family were completely at home in art galleries. Here, we five women enjoying our meal together are all directly descended from my great-grandfather.

Our common ancestor had struggled to feed his eight children by making and selling picture frames. Aged eleven years, my Grandpa had won a scholarship to the prestigious Daniel Stewarts College, in Edinburgh. He told us how, in class, he suffered the humiliation of having to call out his address as 'West Cross Causeway', when his classmates lived in Avenues and Squares. Despite acting as delivery boy for his father in the evenings, a function he hated like poison, Grandpa still managed to win school prizes in Greek, classics and mathematics. On his fifteenth birthday, his father removed him from the school to work full-time in picture framing. Even in his mature years, Grandpa spoke with pain of the humiliation he had felt as a youth, when trudging around the workmen's tenement homes in Edinburgh, hawking framed images of cheap German prints of Bonnie Prince Charlie and Highland Mary. Grandpa tells his own story:

And so, sacrificing the fourth year of the scholarship, I found myself in the back of the shop, cleaning picture glasses, scraping and staining hundreds of oak frames and doing all the life-stemming things that were to lead me into a life of misery for which I was, by nature, never fitted. The picture of the frock-coated, silk-hatted headmaster of the college, actually coming to the shop to enquire from my father why my studies had been interrupted, still remains in my mind. I peeped out from the back shop, and observed the argument between my father and the headmaster, Dr Dunlop. He was trying his best to save my life, and my own father, innocently perhaps, was doing his best to destroy it. Needless to say, my father won.

What would my dear Grandpa or my great-grandfather have felt, could they have seen us five women, joking, laughing, debating and talking together at the Sydney Art Gallery at the dawn of the twenty-first century? I wondered at the amazing leap forward over just a couple of generations in our family. Education, opportunity and good health, together with supportive homes, had been the key to our enhanced living.

How lucky we had all been.